PAUL BRANSOM

Marlin Perkins'
ZOOPARADE ®

To Mark
With all good wishes,
Marlin Perkins

Marlin Perkins'
ZOOPARADE ®

by Marlin Perkins

with color illustrations
by Paul Bransom

black-and-white illustrations
by Seymour Fleishman

RAND McNALLY & COMPANY

Chicago · New York · San Francisco

To my daughter SUZY

*With the hope that her greatest interest in life will give her as
much pleasure and satisfaction as I have received from animals.*

CONTENTS

Why This Book Was Written

I CAN'T REMEMBER my first contact with an animal. My older brothers, however, recall the time when, at two and a half, I was pulled, muddy and nearly drowned, from the water-filled excavation for a house by a neighbor who had investigated the cause of the frantic barking of our little yellow dog. It was our big, black shepherd Rex who first taught me the caution needed by a small boy bent on pulling the ears of a sharp-toothed dog. And Billy, our goat, gave me deep respect for the butting ability of an animal that did not defend itself with its teeth.

When I was five, my father built what we called a "country place," a house on a small farm about three miles from Carthage, Missouri. It wan't long before I had pockets filled with field mice and snakes, land turtles and frogs. And I remember following the hired man as he plowed with our horse, Dan. In the slick, dark earth left in the angle of the deepest part of the furrow I discovered all kinds of surprising, fascinating creatures: earthworms, partially in their subterranean burrows; grubs of various insects; and an occasional mole.

A few years later when I was attending what was then called the Pittsburg Normal School, at Pittsburg, Kansas, the head of the zoology department had a pet bull snake which he allowed the children to handle once in a while. This bull snake held more than average interest for me, and I began haunting the zoology laboratory to find out more about snakes. First I learned the poisonous ones, so that I could recognize and stay away from them, and then the nonpoisonous ones and something of their habits. It wasn't long before I was collecting snakes for the zoology department and myself.

Cages and a place to keep a collection of live animals were sometimes a problem. My aunt, with whom I lived, didn't like to have them in the basement, and so with another boy I kept them secretly in the loft of a neighbor's barn. I don't know yet what would have happened if Mr. Kerr had ever looked behind the bales of hay in the loft and discovered cans and apple boxes filled with snapping turtles, bull frogs, snakes, lizards, and salamanders.

My interest in animals continued through the years of my formal education, and beyond. After two years at the University of Missouri, I took a job at the St. Louis Zoo, and that job led to a career. The more I learned about animals, the more interested in the subject I became. It wasn't long before I was Curator of Reptiles. I owe much of my success to the encouragement and kindly advice of George Vierheller, the Director of the St. Louis Zoo, who gave me my first chance to work with wild animals. It was he who urged me to continue learning about animals and to make the knowledge available to our visitors, for it is the job of the zoo, as an interpretive institution, to tell the animal story.

Zoos tell this story in many ways. It is told on the labels in front of the cages, which, as George Vierheller pointed out, if put together in book form would make a concise natural history text. The story is told in movies which are available for schools, and in guided tours for classroom groups. The story is told in newspapers and magazines, in lecture form at civic organizations and Boy Scout meetings, and on the radio. But perhaps the greatest medium yet devised for telling the animal story is television.

I had heard about television for many years before I saw a telecast program. Then, in 1945 the opportunity to try out television was presented to me. I met Beulah Zachery, a director at WBKB, the only television station in Chicago, and she invited me to bring some of my animals to the studio and talk about them. While there were only three hundred TV sets in the Chicago area then, I was happy to gain experience in using this new medium. It soon seemed to me that this was really the answer. By moving the camera in close, it was possible to get extreme close-ups of the animals, or portions of the animals, and point out characteristics and adaptations which really show and explain how the animals function.

In 1949, Reinald Werrenrath, Jr., brought the mobile unit of NBC to the Lincoln Park Zoo and "Zooparade" was born. At first the program was broadcast locally, and then in 1950 it became a network feature. Sunday after Sunday afternoon our program went out to the nation, and soon we were telling the animal story to millions of Americans. Children like it, and parents tell me that they watch the program with the children as a family venture. To me, this is gratifying.

This book is a continuation of the animal story. Paul Bransom, with his superb paintings, lets you see the animals in a way I know you will appreciate; and Seymour Fleishman, with his black-and-white illustrations, has given you the animals sketched from life at our zoo. And I have tried to give you word pictures of the lives and habits of some of the animals I have known.

MARLIN PERKINS

Marlin Perkins'
ZOOPARADE®

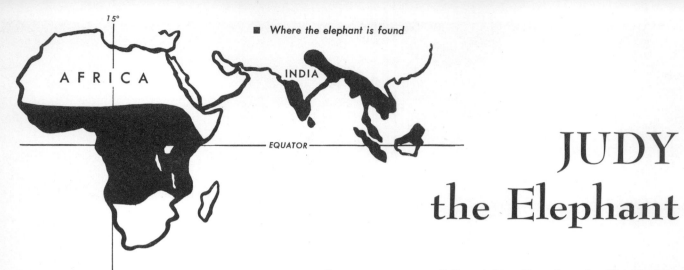

AFRICA 15°

INDIA

■ Where the elephant is found

EQUATOR

JUDY the Elephant

It was a warm July night. People who lived along one of the main boulevards leading into Chicago from the west were having a hard time sleeping. Then, after what they heard coming down the boulevard in the dead of night, few of them wanted to sleep. They hung out of the windows and stared.

Could it be a parade? Yes, it must be a parade, for there was an elephant. But, on looking closer, they saw that with the elephant were police squad cars, motorcycle policemen, reporters and photographers, and men with sharp-pointed elephant hooks.

No, it was not a parade. "Judy," the elephant, was simply moving from the Brookfield Zoo in the western suburbs of Chicago to the Lincoln Park Zoo in the heart of the city. But Judy had her own ideas about changing her home. She had refused to ride in a big truck. In fact, she had almost torn the truck to pieces. So there was nothing to do but walk Judy the eighteen miles separating the two zoos, and call in police to clear the streets ahead of her.

Judy had decided to take her time. She was not in a hurry and probably she wanted to see the sights. It took the procession from eight o'clock at night till four o'clock the next morning to make the trip!

Everyone was surprised Judy acted that way about riding in on the truck. She had always been a good and gentle elephant and minded her keepers. When she got in her new home, she settled down and became a peaceful elephant again.

Judy likes peanuts, cough drops, lump sugar—and marshmallows! Marshmallows are her favorite, and when she sees someone with a bag which she thinks contains marshmallows, she gets down on her knees and begs. Each day she gets a bucket of carrots, apples, and beets. And water! She drinks four bucketfuls in the morning, three more at noon, and twelve at night! She draws the water up in her trunk—which holds almost a gallon—and then sprays it from her trunk into her mouth.

Judy goes in for beauty treatments, too. She gets a manicure frequently. She will place each foot in turn up on a big block of wood, so her toenails can be filed

and polished. Twice a year she is rubbed down with two and a half gallons of neat's-foot oil, to keep her skin from drying out and cracking.

Children who visit Judy may read her history on the outside of her cage:

INDIAN ELEPHANT

(*Elephas maximus*)

RANGE: INDIA, CEYLON, INDO-CHINA AND THE MALAY

This elephant named "Judy" arrived in the U.S. in 1914, when she was about 4 years old. She landed at Norfolk, Va., and became the property of the Stone-Murry Circus. A few years later she was sold to another circus owner, Mr. Augustus J. Jones. She performed in his circus from 1917–1930. She was then purchased by Mr. Wm. Scott, owner of the Bedford Zoo at Manchester, N.H. After a year or two Mr. John T. Benson of Nashua, N.H., purchased her and took her to his privately owned zoo. In 1934 Mr. Benson sold "Judy" to the Brookfield Zoo. In 1943 she was purchased by the Chicago Park District from the Chicago Zoological Society. "Judy" refused to ride the eighteen miles from Brookfield Zoo to Lincoln Park Zoo in a large truck, but did make the trip on foot throughout the night July 2, 1943. She weighs about 3½ tons, and eats about 125 lbs. of timothy hay, 18 lbs. of vegetables, ½ peck of bran and several loaves of bread each day.

But that does not tell all about Judy, and to know about Judy is to know about most elephants in zoos today.

There is no record of how Judy was caught. But in India wild elephants are driven into what is called a "keddah," a large place fenced off especially for this purpose. The people of India catch elephants to use as work animals. The elephants do the work of our big machines, and can even push up big trees by the roots and carry heavy logs on their tusks.

There are only three kinds of elephants—the Indian, the African, and the African pygmy, which seldom grows to be more than six and a half feet tall. The African elephant has larger ears and longer tusks. It has only three toes on each hind foot, while the Indian elephant has four or five. The pygmy has four. Female Indian elephants like Judy have short tusks, or no tusks. But some African male elephants have tusks weighing from 150 to 200 pounds. In Africa elephants are hunted for their tusks, which are of valuable ivory. But in India the government will not allow elephant-hunting for ivory or for sport.

Tusks are really long teeth. The elephant uses them to defend himself and to carry things. He has other teeth, too, each one weighing about six pounds. The skin of elephants is very thick, and yet elephants are bothered by flies and other insects. With their trunks they throw dust over their backs to give themselves some protection. They also take mud baths and allow the mud to cake on their skin to protect them further.

African elephant

Indian elephant

The most interesting thing about the elephant is his trunk. It is a long arm, a nose, a "feeler," and a suction pump all at the same time. It contains some 40,000 muscles, and with it the elephant can pick up the smallest peanut or the largest man.

There are many mistaken stories about elephants. One is that elephants live to be very old. Actually they do not live so long as human beings and are old at forty-five. There are stories, too, of their remarkable memory—how they never forget. But this is no more true of the elephant than of most other animals.

When older people see an elephant they are reminded of Jumbo, the biggest elephant ever captured. Jumbo was an African elephant that weighed six tons—as much as three big automobiles. P. T. Barnum, the circus man, bought him for $10,000 and brought him to America in 1882, where he created a sensation.

In their wild state elephants live in family groups. In zoos most of them live alone. But for Judy and most other elephants in captivity, zoo life is easier, because they are provided with the proper amount of food and shelter, care when they are ill, and other attention.

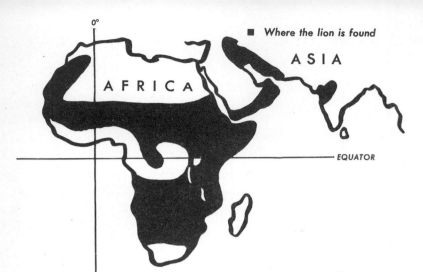

DILLINGER
the Lion

WHEN HE WAS a roly-poly lion cub, they called him King. He gave promise of growing into a big, handsome lion, and when he was two years old, his owner decided to try to teach him tricks.

But King showed from the first that he did not want to jump through hoops, sit on chairs, place his forepaws on boxes, or do other things that circus lions do. Instead of learning tricks, he growled at his owner and showed his long, sharp teeth. When a stick was pushed at him to make him back up, he seized the stick with his teeth and splintered it.

One day he leaped on his owner and injured the man so badly that he had to be taken to the hospital. From his bed there King's owner sent word to the keeper to get rid of the lion. He was through trying to teach such a difficult animal tricks.

When King came to the Lincoln Park Zoo, he had such a poor reputation that the zoo men did not think he deserved to be called by the name of King. So they renamed him Dillinger, after the notorious bad man and outlaw. The name Dillinger seemed to fit him. He made it plain from the start that he did not want to be friends with the keepers or with anyone else. He just wanted to be fed and left alone.

But Wilson (Willie) Renner, one of the keepers, had had long experience with lions. He liked lions that were friendly and he started out to try to make friends with Dillinger. Every time he passed Dillinger's cage he would talk to him. Just talked quietly so that Dillinger would become familiar with his voice. He would say, "Nice old boy," "Come and get your meat, Dillinger," or something like that.

Then, after a long time, Dillinger began to prick up his ears when Willie talked to him. One day he walked to the bars of his cage and began to rub his body against them.

Willie knew this sign. Dillinger wanted to be friends at last. So Willie reached in and touched Dillinger's back. He said quietly, "You like your back scratched, don't you?" Dillinger appeared to enjoy it. Later the keeper scratched Dillinger's head, talking to him all the time. Finally he could pet Dillinger from head to tail.

16

He would say, "I'm going to scratch your tail," and Dillinger would switch his tail within reach.

When it came time to cut Dillinger's claws and the matted fur of his mane, Willie did not have to rope him and tie him up. He just petted him with one hand, talking all the time in a low voice, and cut his claws and mane with the other.

"I had to keep talking to him," explains Willie Renner. "Just like a trainer talks to his horse. All animals seem to respond to a familiar voice better than to anything else."

Everyone at the zoo was amazed. No one had believed Dillinger would ever be a friendly lion. But he did become one of the friendliest—to Willie. No one else dared get near his cage. . . . Dillinger is no longer with us, but he will long be remembered as an example of how even a fierce lion can be made to become friends with a man.

Lions born in zoos or captured in the wilds while very young usually are easily tamed. But as they mature, their disposition changes. Though some retain gentleness toward their keepers, in general they become untrustworthy and dangerous.

The lion has been known to man from the earliest times in history. For centuries he was known as the "King of Beasts." When men became more familiar with the lion, it was seen that he was not always a courageous animal. But all admit that the lion, with his great mane and magnificent head, has a kingly appearance. His voice is grand and striking. His deep-toned roars, when repeated in quick succession, each one louder than the one before, dying away into five or six muffled sounds like distant thunder, probably startle the other animals of the wild.

The lion is found in Africa, Mesopotamia, Iran, and some parts of western India. The African lion is the largest, and a full-grown male may measure ten feet in length from his nose to the tip of his tail. The tail itself is about three feet long. A lioness is smaller and has no mane.

The lion's mane is darker than his body and begins to grow when he is about three years old. When the lion is five or six, he has a full mane. On the tip of his tail is a tuft of hair. This covers a sharp, horny point, which is called the "thorn." There is some doubt about the purpose of this "thorn," but some think it grows there so that a lion can make himself furious when he lashes his tail against his flanks. In such a state he may be willing to fight anything. To me the "thorn" remains a mystery.

A lion and lioness will pair off and remain together. When the cubs are born, usually three, the father lion helps raise them. He provides food and teaches them to hunt. Cubs remain with their parents until they are about three years old.

When they are born, the cubs, especially the males, have dark spots on their bodies. But, as they grow older, their color changes to a yellowish brown and may vary from a deep red or chestnut brown to silvery gray. The markings disappear.

Lions hunt in pairs and sometimes in small troops, usually made up of the lion and lioness and their full-grown cubs. But sometimes older lions join together in a hunt. They commonly hunt at night, like other members of the cat tribe, but in some wild and desolate regions they may be seen out during the day.

The first lesson in hunting which a baby lion gets is learning to pounce on its mother's swishing tail. In cages at the zoo even the older lions like this sort of pouncing exercise. When we place a balloon in the cage, they play just like house cats. They bat the balloon around with their huge paws. When it bursts they look puzzled.

At 4:00 P.M., six days a week, the lions are fed at the zoo. Each one gets about twelve pounds of raw meat plus the vitamins a lion should have to be healthy and strong. On Saturdays they get liver, and on Mondays no food at all. This is "fast day" for all the Big Cats.

This careful feeding helps the lions to live longer in captivity than they do in the scrub forests and plains. They get the proper food during their older years when, in the wild state, they would be unable to capture the animals necessary for their welfare. In captivity they have more beautiful manes, too, as there are no thorns and bushes to tear out the hair. A zoo lion may live to be twenty-five years old—a ripe old age.

SHAH and SHEBA the Cheetahs

SHAH, THE CHEETAH, sits in his cage, a faraway look in his eyes. He seems to be gazing back a thousand years. Once his ancestors were the pets of princes and kings. They wore collars of rare metals set with jewels. They were trained for the chase and could outrun any other animal.

As Shah stares into space over the heads of the people standing before his cage in the zoo, suddenly he hears a birdlike chirp from the next cage. It is a noise such as a starling might make. Shah instantly is all attention. The chirping sound is from Sheba, the female cheetah next door. She is excited and is running back and forth in her cage, stopping now and then to look out at the crowd.

Shah is on his feet and he, too, looks out.

In front of Sheba's cage is a little girl about six years old, dressed in a snowsuit, her cheeks rosy from the outdoor cold and her eyes sparkling.

Both Shah and Sheba now are bounding back and forth, pausing only to rub against the bars, all the time watching the little girl. The mother places a protective arm around the child and draws her close.

"Don't be frightened, ma'am," says the keeper. "Cheetahs pay little attention to older people, but whenever a child about your daughter's age comes here they begin to act excited like this. They are always interested in children—why we are not quite sure. Maybe they are attracted by their small size. The animals look as if they wanted to romp and play with your daughter. They might even be as gentle as kittens and never harm her. But we don't know, and we certainly are never going to take a chance and let a cheetah loose to find out."

The mother looks with renewed interest at the two graceful animals. The little girl wants to stay. But her mother only shakes her head doubtfully and leads the child away.

When cheetahs have been tamed, they are much like dogs and cats. They seem to enjoy the attention of their masters.

The cheetah has been called the "Hunting Leopard." It is said that many tame hunting leopards become perfectly gentle and docile. They will rub affec-

20

tionately against their masters' knees, purring all the time like so many large cats.

The cheetah is about the same size as the leopard, but not the same shape. It has a longer body and legs. In coloring and marking, too, the cheetah resembles the leopard somewhat, but its black and brown spots are round and have no light-colored centers. The spots stand out clearly on the yellowish brown background, being smallest on the head and largest on the tail. At the end of the tail they become rings.

The cheetah has a small head with two black lines on its face running from the upper lip to the corner of the eyes. Only the cheetah has such markings. Its claws, too, cannot be withdrawn like those of other members of the cat family, and when the cheetah walks around in its cage, one can hear the clicking of these claws on the concrete floor.

The cheetah can be recognized at once by its long, straight legs. The legs look much like those of the tall and slender hunting dog, the greyhound. In fact, the cheetah often is called the "greyhound of the cat family." With its long legs the cheetah can run very fast, as fast as seventy miles an hour for a short distance. It can bound twenty feet. The cheetah hunts by sight and can see its prey from a long distance.

For centuries the cheetah has been used in Persia and India for hunting. History tells that the first king to use the cheetah for the chase was Hushing, King of Persia, 'way back in 865 B.C. After that the fame of the cheetah as a hunter spread, and Mongol princes sometimes took as many as a thousand cheetahs with them when they hunted deer and other small game. When an Oriental king or prince went for a stroll, he would have two cheetahs on the leash.

The cheetah is a native of both Asia and Africa. In India, where the cheetah was once so popular, there are few left today. In their native state cheetahs live in low, rocky hills near the plains on which antelopes range. Antelopes are their favorite food, but they also hunt rabbits and other small game.

Wild cheetahs hunt in pairs or small groups. Before a hunt they all meet at a certain tree. This tree can be recognized by hunters because it shows the markings of the animals' claws, for cheetahs always "manicure" or file down their claws, when overlong, especially before hunting. On discovering such a tree, men who want to capture the wild cheetahs lay traps here. Despite the speed with which a cheetah can run, in the wild state it is often the prey of larger, stronger animals.

In a zoo cheetahs like Shah and Sheba eat about three and a half pounds of meat a day. They also are given vitamins. Just as with the lions and tigers and other members of the cat family, they are given nothing to eat on Mondays. This is a "fast day" and serves to give their stomachs a rest.

Shah and Sheba will someday be mated, and we hope there will be baby cheetahs. Cheetah cubs do not look like the older animals, for they are solid gray. They do not get their full markings until they are several months old.

Now Shah and Sheba are getting better acquainted. Their keeper puts them together every morning, and leaves them in the same cage until feeding time, about four o'clock. Then they go back to their separate cages to eat, doze, and daydream of some small girl or boy stopping to admire them.

140°

NEW GUINEA

20°

AUSTRALIA

DOTTY
the Kangaroo

DOTTY LIKES PEANUTS. She gets only a few—maybe two or three a day—but she sits up on her hind legs and tail and shells the nuts and eats the kernels with relish.

Usually one does not think of kangaroos eating peanuts. Monkeys and elephants, yes. But not kangaroos. Still, there is no reason why kangaroos should not like peanuts. The animals live on grass, herbs, and young tree shoots in their native state.

Peanuts are a sort of treat, or dessert, for Dotty of the Lincoln Park Zoo, who is really a wallaroo or rock kangaroo. She looks forward to them after she eats her hay, raw vegetables, and oats.

Where Dotty came from, in Australia, there are fifty known kinds of kangaroos. Some live in Australia proper and others in Tasmania, New Guinea, and near-by islands. In size the animals range from the rare little rat kangaroo to the giant red and the great gray kangaroo. Some are known as wallabies and others as wallaroos.

These strange animals are all called "marsupials." This means that a mother carries her young ones in a pouch or "marsupium." The only marsupial in the United States is the Virginia opossum, but in Australia there are more than three hundred kinds of marsupials. Some live in trees, some on the ground, and some under the earth. They include not only the kangaroo, but a "wolf," a little "bear" known as the koala—and affectionately called the "Teddy bear"—and "rats" and many others.

Long before written history the marsupials were to be found in Asia, Europe, South America, and other parts of the world. It is believed that Australia became separated from Asia by seas and oceans, and the marsupials in the land "down under" did not develop beyond their present stage of life.

That is why the thing that interests most people about the kangaroo is the pouch of the mother where she carries her baby. The baby is called a "joey." When born, it is but an inch long (about the size of a peanut) and is blind and

24

without hair. It has very long forearms, which enable it to crawl up its mother's fur and into her pouch. This is its home until it is about four months old. Here, in this snug nursery, "Joey" lives on milk. When his eyes open and he grows bigger, he can sit up and poke his little head out of the pouch and look around at the world.

Then comes the time to leave the pouch. "Joey" crawls out and has his first meal of solid food. This consists of grass, leaves of vines, and young trees which he snips off with his very sharp lower teeth.

For a time he can hop in and out of his mother's pouch, but soon he grows too big and cannot get back in. This home becomes closed to him forever. But still during his younger months, whenever he is in danger, he runs to his mother and tries to hide in her pouch. Often he will just stick his head in and feel that he is safe.

Kangaroos have powerful hind legs which enable them to hop as far as twenty feet. By this hopping action they can move swiftly among rocks and tall grass and make it difficult for birds and beasts of prey to capture them. They travel as fast as twenty to thirty miles an hour. On each hind foot, too, is a fighting weapon. It is a long and sharp toenail, like a bayonet, on the largest toe. An unarmed man is no match for the bigger kangaroos, nor are many animals.

The kangaroo's long, thick tail is really a third hind "leg." When he is sitting up, he rests on his two hind legs and tail much as a camera rests on a photographer's tripod. With his tail the kangaroo pushes himself forward when he is eating grass. When he hops, his tail sticks straight out behind and acts as a balance or rudder. The kangaroo's forearms, when he is fully grown, are not nearly so large or long as his hind legs.

The red kangaroo is the largest of all the kangaroos. He stands as high as a man, possibly a little higher than the average man, as most of the red kangaroos are about six feet tall. They live on the plains and in dry inland regions. They have a foolish way of stopping and looking back when pursued. At such times they rotate their large ears to catch sound coming from any direction. But when they stop this way, their enemies can draw nearer. We can be glad they have this habit since it makes it easier for photographers to get good pictures of them. When it rains and the ground becomes soggy, these kangaroos can easily be captured, for they sink in the mud and cannot hop away. While the male kangaroo of this species is red, the female is a sort of bluish color.

The next largest type is the gray kangaroo. These prefer the open forests and plains. Both the male and female are of a grayish or grayish brown color. The gray kangaroo is believed to have been the first seen by Captain Cook, the

British explorer, when he cast anchor at the mouth of the Endeavour River, North Queensland, in 1770. He described it as a mouse-colored animal as long as a greyhound. The natives called it a *"kanguru."* However, some say that Captain Cook actually saw a whip-tailed kangaroo, which is smaller than the great gray kangaroo.

Smaller than the red or gray kangaroo is the black-faced kangaroo that lives in the bush and scrublands. Then there are the wallaroos, or rock kangaroos, such as our own Dotty. They are thick-set and powerful and live among the rocky hills. They can go a long time without water. The wallaroos of New South Wales and southern Queensland are the best known of this group.

The next in size are the wallabies. These smaller kangaroos live in the dense scrub or among the tropical palm bushes. Some prefer the open forest country. Here in the forests, too, are the tree kangaroos, or tree wallabies. These have become scarce.

The rat kangaroo is the smallest of all. They are interesting little creatures. With their tails they can carry bundles of hay with which they build their nests. They are now almost extinct.

Kangaroos feed in flocks. While eating, they are guarded by the older males, who keep a sharp outlook and warn of approaching danger. The natural enemies of the kangaroo are the dingo, or Australian wild dog, the wedge-tailed eagle, and the python snake.

Australians are proud of their kangaroos and now seek to protect them. One appears on their national emblem.

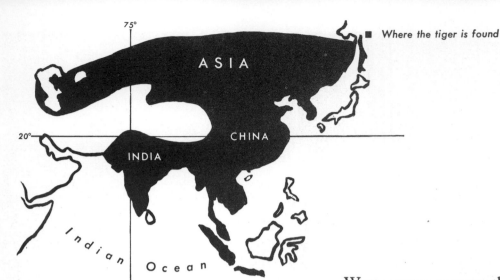

BARA
the Tiger

WORD WENT AROUND the Bronx Zoo in New York City that four baby tigers had just been born in the lion house. Visitors were not allowed to see them for fear of frightening the mother. In trying to protect her cubs in such a small cage she might harm them.

In her native land the tigress is known as a good and affectionate mother. But when cubs are born in zoos, it has been found best to take them from the mother and raise them in a nursery. In this way they grow to be healthier animals and in most cases are much more tame.

The problem at the Bronx Zoo was to get the little tigers out of the cage without hurting them. The best way was to get the mother out first. To do this, a door leading from her cage to the next one was opened, and the tiger mother's daily food was placed there. When she went in to eat, she was shut off from her cubs.

The cubs, their eyes still closed—they are blind for nine days after birth—were then carefully removed. They were beautiful little creatures with the same color and stripes as the older tigers.

At the Bronx Zoo several litters of cubs from the same mother had already been raised. At first the little ones were fed milk with an eye dropper. As they grew older, they learned to drink milk out of a bottle with a nipple on it. They had a formula just like other babies.

After about six weeks they were fed meat. By this time they were romping and playing with one another just like kittens. When the cubs grew to be about eight months old, it was time to put them into cages. Later they were sent to other zoos.

One of these cubs, named Bara, came to the Lincoln Park Zoo. Bara is the Hindu word for the numeral 12 and means that this tiger was the twelfth one born to the Bronx Zoo mother while she was in captivity.

Bara has grown into a handsome tigress. Her fur is orange-yellow, barred with black cross stripes. She keeps herself clean by licking her fur with her rough

tongue and by "washing" herself with her forepaw—just like any pet house cat.

The tiger is one of the hardest of all large cats to tame. For hundreds of years his ancestors had to live by the law of the jungle where only the strongest survived. Even in captivity a tiger, when he reaches about eight months or a year, seems to feel that he has to be independent and cannot trust any other animal —not even men who have been kind to him. Some tigers raised in captivity remain tame throughout their lives, but their keepers never cease to watch them carefully at all times.

This fierceness can be understood when they are born in the wilds. For then the mother is careful to teach her young to hunt when they are just babies. First she waves her tail back and forth so they will learn to pounce on it. Then she goes out with the young tigers and shows them how to hunt smaller animals. They follow her example until they become expert hunters themselves.

The tiger resembles the lion more than any other of the Big Cats, but the tiger is color-striped and has no mane. The tiger is believed by many the animal entitled to the name "King of Beasts." Usually he is called the "Lord of the Forests." He does not fear to attack any other animal. Unlike the lion, who prefers company on the hunt, the tiger often hunts alone. When tracks are seen leading directly to a watering place, you can be sure they are tiger tracks. No other animal approaches the watering place in a straight line—they all zigzag or go in a roundabout way on the lookout for enemies. Not the tiger. He shows that he is afraid of nothing.

Tigers are found only in Asia, where they live in grassy plains and jungle swamps. The striped pattern of their bodies is Nature's way of making it hard to see them in the jungle. The stripes are often mistaken for the shadows of tree branches on the ground. While tigers do not often go into the water, they are good swimmers. In the delta of the River Ganges in India it is said that tigers swim from one island to another to change their hunting grounds.

Tigers are full grown when they are four years old. They can climb trees if necessary, like other members of the cat tribe, but they hunt on the ground. They slink along, close to the earth, when approaching the animal they are stalking.

There are many tales of the great strength of tigers. It is said they can carry a four-hundred-pound bullock, even while leaping over a wall or fence. One hunter reported that he had seen a tiger carrying such a large load for three hundred yards through a dense thicket, never allowing the bullock to touch the ground.

There is no creature from India to the Malay Peninsula that the natives fear as they do the tiger, with the exception of the crocodile. They know that old or injured tigers in hunger sometimes lose fear of man with his death-dealing weapons and turn man-eaters. The natives keep as far away from the tiger as possible.

Bara, in our zoo, is a Bengal, or southern, tiger. Sometimes she looks so gentle that it would appear she would welcome a friendly pat. But her keepers take no chances. She has just reached that age where no one can tell just what she may do.

Perhaps when she is older, with all the kind attention given her, her fifteen pounds of meat a day brought to her, and her cage kept warm and clean, she will actually become gentle and show that she is pleased by the easy life she leads.

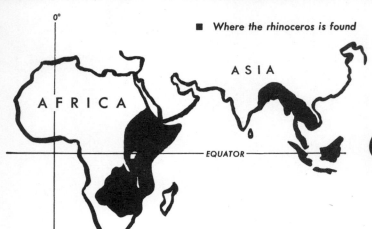

0°

ASIA

AFRICA

EQUATOR

GEORGIE-JOE
the Rhinoceros

WHENEVER A BABY ANIMAL is born in a zoo, there is always great excitement. Everything is done to make the mother comfortable and to see that she is not disturbed by people who are just curious.

Sometimes it would appear that a young prince or princess was being born. Doctors and nurses—really, veterinarians and keepers—wait anxiously for the event. Word is sent out to the press, and soon photographers will come and take pictures. Everyone breathes a sigh of relief when the bulletin announces:

"Mother and baby doing well."

Such a news flash meant a lot more than usual to zoo men all over the country a few years ago when the newborn baby was a rhinoceros. For never before had a baby been born to African rhinoceros parents in a zoo.

So it would be hard to imagine the excitement around the Brookfield Zoo— on the outskirts of Chicago—when little Georgie-Joe came into the world.

Georgie-Joe weighed ninety pounds at birth, which is big for a baby. But one must understand that Georgie-Joe's mother was quite large—in fact, she belonged to a family which, next to that of the elephant and the hippopotamus, is the largest of the land animals. She weighed 2,200 pounds—more than two ordinary horses.

Georgie-Joe was given the very best care. He lived on his mother's milk and after two weeks began to experiment, in addition, with tender roots and the other solid foods that rhinos like. On the end of his nose was a small button which in time would grow into a long, sharp horn. Behind this first horn would sprout another, not so long. All black rhinos have these two horns.

Georgie-Joe grew and grew. At eight months of age he was weaned, and finally he was sold to another zoo.

Then Mother Rhino gave birth to a second son. The excitement around the zoo was almost as great as before. The new baby had already been named before he was born. He was called "Young Robert," in honor of Robert Ringling, the circus owner. Mr. Ringling had said he wanted the next rhino born at the zoo—

32

if such an event ever happened again—and he was happy to get Young Robert, who became a part of the menagerie in his circus.

There have been baby rhinos born to Indian rhino parents in zoos, but they have never been raised. So Georgie-Joe and Young Robert have the distinction of being the only rhinos born and reared in captivity.

Georgie-Joe and Young Robert belong to the kind known as the African black rhinoceros. These are not actually black, nor is the other type in Africa—the so-called white rhino—really white. The white rhino usually has a whitish color because, after being in the water, he likes to roll in white alkali dust, which dries on his hide. The white rhino is larger than the black type and has a longer main horn.

The "horn" is one of the interesting things about the rhino. It is really neither horn nor bone, but consists of long bristles or hairs which grow out from the skin of the nose. They stick together in a hard, solid mass, which is as sharp and tough as actual horn or bone. The rhino uses his horn to dig up roots and to protect himself.

The hide of the rhino is very thick, yet tender unless it is dry. The rhino can feel an insect bite and wallows in mud to get relief from the pain of these bites. There are small birds, known as tickbirds, that sit on the rhino's back and pick off the ticks. These birds, too, warn the rhino of the approach of an enemy, for the huge animal does not see well with his small eyes. But he has a very keen hearing and sense of smell.

Despite their huge size and awkward appearance, rhinos are light on their feet and very swift. They can run as fast as race horses at the start, but they can keep up this speed for only a short distance. They can "turn on a dime" and charge back with another burst of speed.

The rhino is a fierce fighter. He seems unafraid to charge anything in his path. He lowers his head, his little tail stands straight up, he gives a snort or two, and runs head-on toward his enemy. When he is angry, lions and leopards and even elephants avoid him. His sharp horn can cause a lot of damage.

Some people who have gone into the wilds to study the rhino say that his fierce charges at anything strange are, many times a fake. The rhinos snort, lift their tails, lower their heads, and dash forward. But if the man or beast who is being charged will stand still and not move from the path of the rhino, Mr. Rhino will stop a few feet away or turn aside. But this is a dangerous experiment, and except for Osa Johnson, the wife of Martin Johnson, photographer of wild animals, no others dared try it. Mrs. Johnson claimed she had proved to her own satisfaction that the theory was true.

African rhinos like to eat rough, thorny leaves, twigs, and grasses which they find in the foothill plains. Elephant grass, which grows twice as tall as a man, is a favorite food.

The other rhinos are the Asiatic rhinos, which have only one horn. They include the Indian, Javan, and Sumatran, or hairy, rhino.

The Indian rhino has only one horn, which is not more than a foot long and not so good as a weapon, but he is much larger than any other rhino. He has large, chisel-like teeth in his lower jaw, which serve as his fighting weapons. He also has a thick skin which reminds one of the armor worn by the knights of the Middle Ages. This skin, or hide, is studded and lies in folds just like plates of armor. Yet these heavy sections of hide are so placed that the rhino can move his head and legs with ease. He may weigh twice as much as his African cousin.

Today the great Indian rhino is found only in the Refuge of Assam, and another area of giant grass, in northern India. Here the animals find the green, sweet-tasting grasses which they like. It is believed there are only about three hundred of these animals now left. All are under government supervision.

In captivity the rhino, like other animals, lives longer. Some grow to be forty years old, or more. Perhaps those in the zoos and circuses miss some of the things they were accustomed to in the wilds. They may miss their small friends, the tickbirds, that sit on their backs and pick off the troublesome ticks, and warn them of danger.

But in captivity rhinos, of course, have no ticks, nor are they ever in danger.

Indian rhinos

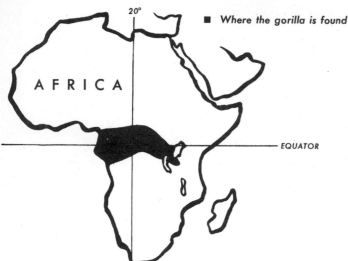

AFRICA

20°

■ *Where the gorilla is found*

EQUATOR

SINBAD
the Gorilla

IN THE LARGEST CAGE of the Monkey House at the Lincoln Park Zoo—the cage of honor, as you will see—Sinbad sits in a corner nibbling on a stalk of celery and glancing out now and then at the crowd in front.

Sinbad is something of a show-off, like a small boy. When he thinks he is being noticed, he will jump up and grab the bar of a swinging trapeze in his cage, fly through the air and land on a shelf, and quick as lightning be up on the second trapeze. All the time he will dart quick glances out to see if he is attracting attention. If he finds his audience is not appreciating him, he will drop to the floor and retire to his corner to continue eating.

Sinbad is a gorilla—and one for whom I have a great affection. I can never forget how as a baby, hardly larger than a house cat, he clung to me, a spindle-legged little fellow, whimpering and miserable. I became his "mother" then, at the moment he snuggled up to me and his little arms went around my neck.

This was back in 1948 when, as head of the Lincoln Park Zoological Expedition, I flew to the French Cameroons in search of more gorillas for our zoo. We went to the same place—Yaoundé, the capital of the Cameroons in French Equatorial Africa—where in 1930 we had found the famed gorilla, Bushman.

At the Presbyterian Mission I first saw the baby gorilla which later was to become known as Sinbad. He was nervous and upset because of his strange surroundings and because he missed his mother. He had been poorly fed and was very thin. He was about nine months old, weighed just ten pounds, and, worst of all, had a bad cold.

Sinbad and I took to each other from the start. From then on I was with him every minute. I held him in my arms during the day, wiping his runny little nose with my pocket handkerchief. I fed him a baby formula of Karo sirup and milk. I gave him multiple-vitamin capsules.

On the second day his cold was gone. On the third day I gave him a bath with soap and water. He smelled clean now and he seemed more contented.

36

But he still clung to me and at night he slept near me on a cot, tightly hugging a rag doll I had made for him from a towel.

After three weeks in Yaoundé our expedition was at an end. Besides Sinbad we had secured three other gorillas—Irving Young and Rajah and a female, Lotus. They were young, too, but they did not need the attention that Sinbad did. So, on the airplane journey back to the United States, Sinbad and I were always together.

On our arrival at the zoo October 1, 1948, Sinbad had gained a little and now weighed eleven pounds. But I had a serious problem. I had many other things to do and I could not spare the time to "mother" Sinbad as much as I would have liked. I therefore turned him over to Roy Hoff, and gradually the little fellow began to think of Keeper Hoff as his "mother." I visited him less and less often and I grew a little sad as I saw his affection being transferred to someone else. But he still responds to me when I go to his cage.

Roy Hoff plays with Sinbad just as Keeper Eddie Robinson used to play with Bushman. Roy can make Sinbad laugh by rolling him over on his back and tickling him in the ribs. Sinbad likes this, and his laugh is like nothing you have ever heard before—a sort of low gargling sound far down in his throat.

Sinbad lives in the cage once occupied by Bushman, who for twenty years was "King of the Zoo." Bushman, whose name came from the Bulu word for gorilla, was the largest in captivity—he weighed 550 pounds and stood six feet two inches tall. He was without doubt the most valuable single animal of his kind in any zoo.

Until his death in 1951 Bushman was the most popular of all our zoo animals. In his honor we have named the Monkey House "Bushman Hall."

Now the stripling, Sinbad, who is almost one-fourth the size of the great Bushman, promises one day to become Bushman's successor in popularity with the children and grownups who visit the Lincoln Park Zoo. He is only five years old and he will not be a full-grown gorilla for another six years or so.

Gorillas are the largest of the so-called manlike apes. They are to be found only in western and equatorial Africa. Sinbad is a lowland gorilla. All gorillas in zoos today are lowland gorillas, except one in the Bronx Zoo. This one is known as a mountain gorilla and came from Albert National Park in the Belgian Congo. Mountain gorillas differ from those of the lowlands in that they have a longer coat of hair.

While a gorilla usually walks on all fours, his hands doubled under so he actually walks on his knuckles, he can walk erect like a man. His arms hang halfway down below his knees when he is standing. He is a powerful animal, more powerful than a man. Many have wondered what would happen if a gorilla and a man were placed together in a wrestling or a boxing ring. The man would not have a chance.

The gorilla has a ferocious look. His forehead is low and sloping, his nostrils are widespread, and his eyes deep-set. The black skin of his face is shiny and without hair. Like others of the ape family he has no tail. The soles of his feet are broad, short, and flat. His hands appear almost like human hands.

Despite his brutal look the gorilla is not so vicious as many think him. He will fight to the death, but only to protect his family, or when wounded or cornered. When approached, he will stand erect and beat his breast with his hands, making a deep hollow sound like that of a drum. Or he will scream a warning.

But if a man will stand his ground and scream back at the gorilla, the chances are the animal will turn away. He does not want to fight unless necessary.

Gorillas travel in family groups consisting of one male and several females with their young. They hunt fruits, bamboo shoots, berries, green leaves, wild sugar cane, and wild vegetables.

At night Papa Gorilla sits at the foot of a tree, on guard against danger. His family is in the tree, sleeping in a rough nest made of branches and lined with leaves. If it is cold, Papa Gorilla may cover himself with leaves.

People who watch Sinbad and the other gorillas at our zoo eat are astonished when they learn that a mature gorilla dines on as much as twenty-two pounds of food each day. Here is a typical gorilla menu: Apples, celery, lettuce, oranges, grapefruit, bananas, grapes, raisins, boiled yams and white potatoes, whole-wheat bread, malt extract, brewers' yeast, uncooked green beans, carrots, other seasonable fruits and vegetables, and lots of milk. No wonder Sinbad seems quite contented with his zoo home!

110°

60°

NORTH
AMERICA

SALLY
the Grizzly Bear

THIS IS A STORY of three little bears. They really are little bears—grizzly bear cubs. There are a Papa Bear and a Mamma Bear, of course, and they will be in the story, too—especially the Mamma Bear, Sally.

At first we did not know how many cubs there were. Sally had gone into her dark den in the rear of the outdoor bear cage shortly after Christmas. We knew something was going to happen, so we had placed Mike, the male bear, in an adjoining cage. Strict orders were given that nothing be done to disturb Sally.

The cubs were born around January 3. All grizzly bear cubs are born just about this time. It is strange, but true, that when grizzly cubs come into the world, you can be very sure it is within a day or two of this date. This applies to cubs born in their native wilds, as well as those born in captivity.

So when Sally did not come out of her den, we knew she had cubs. How many? Well, it would be weeks, perhaps months, before we knew. We did not try to find out. This would have caused Sally to seek to protect her cubs in the way Nature had taught her. In doing so she might have harmed them. But we did listen to the whining of the cubs and guessed there were at least three.

Everyone was anxious to see the cubs. Then, on a bright day two and a half months later, Sally came out. First she looked around carefully. Then, evidently finding everything all right, she gave her cubs some kind of signal, and out they came! Or rather, out they tumbled.

Yes, there were three of them, and they blinked in the bright daylight, curious about their new surroundings. They were fat and chubby and full of fun. The big new world did not frighten them. They rolled about and played with one another. Sally watched them carefully, now and then nudging one with her nose to be sure he was all right. When one little fellow became too rough in his play, she picked him up with her teeth by the scruff of his neck and carried him to the other side of the cage. He appeared to know right away that this treatment meant for him to be good.

40

Day by day the cubs grew stronger and more daring. They investigated all parts of the cage and—notwithstanding all that has been written about grizzly bears not climbing trees—they did climb a tree trunk which was in the center of the cage! It is true that older grizzly bears, because of their great size, seldom climb trees, but we have found that cubs will climb trees until they are about two years old.

So the old-time "b'ar" hunters, who told so many outlandish stories about their meetings with grizzly bears, were almost right when they claimed that they were safe from these animals if they could get into a tree—only I wouldn't want to put their theory to a test!

Bear mothers are among the best mothers in the animal kingdom. And Sally is one of the best mothers at our zoo. For many years now she has reared her cubs, bringing a litter into the world every two years, as is the custom with grizzly bears.

While full-grown bears like Mike and Sally can never be tamed, it must be admitted that they are very smart. They learn to do many tricks of their own that will cause visitors to toss peanuts, Crackerjack, or candied apples into their cage.

One of the first things Sally does is to teach her cubs such tricks. She sits up on her haunches, and holds out her arms, sometimes waving them. She may lie on her back, or roll her head, or walk around in a small circle. She puts on an "act," and this never fails to attract the things she likes, especially sweet things. The cubs are not long in finding this out and imitating their mother.

When we think of grizzly bears in their native haunts, we are reminded of bear hunters, mountain men, frontiersmen, and Indians. Especially Indians, for the bear was one of the most useful animals for the Indian. The grizzly bear provided him with a warm bearskin robe for winter. Bear's oil or grease was used for mixing his war paint, for rubbing on his bow, and for anointing his hair. Bear claws and teeth were made into highly prized ornaments.

The Indian admired the grizzly bear for his strength and courage. Many Indians would not harm a bear. Often the bear was the sacred animal of a tribe. Bears, too, were supposed to have unusual knowledge, especially of herbs and plants useful for food and for curing sickness. Indian medicine men followed what they called the "bear trail" in seeking herbs and plants that would make them more proficient in curing the sick.

The white man found the grizzly bear in the region from the Rocky Mountains north through Canada to Alaska and named him *"Ursus horribilis,"* or "dreadful bear." While the grizzly usually would not bother a man, if he were wounded he became one of the most savage of the wild animals of America.

The bear expresses himself with a loud whuff, or a growl, and when angry he gives a short roar. He will seize his victim, biting and clawing all the time. Many old "b'ar" hunters have said that when they lay quietly, the grizzly bear would not hurt them, although he might sniff them and walk over them. But you can be sure that as soon as the bear got a short distance away, the hunter was up a tree!

Male bears grow to be from six and one-half to seven feet long. They weigh from 350 to 900 pounds. Their claws are long and sharp and they cannot draw them in as cats do. The print of a bear's hind foot in the snow or damp ground looks much like that of a man.

The grizzly bear's fur is thick and shaggy, the tail is short, and the body appears clumsy. But he can move swiftly when he wants to. He eats fruits, roots, and other vegetable matter, honey, insects, and meat. The grizzly does not hibernate, or sleep in the winter, as some people think. When the mother bear is going to have cubs, however, she goes into seclusion, and sometimes does not eat for six weeks or more.

Grizzlies are closely related to the great brown bear of Russia and the Kodiak bear of Alaska. Most of the few grizzly bears left in the United States are now protected in the national parks.

Grizzly bears often go about alone, but in the summer months they are to be found in pairs or small herds. In captivity the male and female are together part of the time. When Sally's cubs are a year old, they will be placed in their own cages, and Mike will return to Sally's cage. Then, on some January 3 when visitors are around the zoo, they will find the outdoor cage empty, but they can be sure that in the dark little den in the rear Sally is mothering her newborn cubs. And again we will wonder how many cubs there are, and what they are like.

BUBBLES and TILLY
the Otters

IF THE DAY is dark and gloomy and everything seems to go wrong and you need cheering up, just take a trip to your zoo and watch the otters at play. You won't feel blue long, and it won't matter any more to you how dismal the weather is outside.

There appear to be no creatures more happy and cheerful than otters. They seem really just to enjoy living. It does not make any difference whether they are on the banks of some stream in their native haunts or in their cages at the zoo. They are usually playing and they go about having fun with such vigor and abandon that anyone watching them cannot help but realize what happy, contented creatures they are.

Let us take Bubbles, for instance. Bubbles is the older of a pair of otters in the Lincoln Park Zoo. The other one is Tilly. They have their own swimming pool in the basement of the Reptile House. The water is kept at a temperature of eighty degrees. Their cage is large, with a glass front to keep the visitors from being splashed with water when Bubbles and Tilly play. Inside the cage there is a concrete "beach," sloping down to the water, and a wooden bench on which the two can rest and sleep—when they have time.

They spend most of their day playing in and out of the water. But along about the middle of the afternoon—around three o'clock—they grow serious. Bubbles may come out of the water and shake herself and then go up to the little door in the rear of the cage. She gets as close to the door as she can, waiting and listening. Tilly comes up right beside her.

Soon they hear footsteps, and they evidently know that it is Keeper John Fettes, bringing their food. They grow excited and begin to make funny little whining sounds. They have worked up an excellent appetite now and are ready to eat.

The small door opens. John Fettes slips in two trays containing fish and dog food—the regular kind of canned dog food. Bubbles starts eating from her tray and Tilly from hers. It does not take them long to clean the trays, and they

44

most certainly do not appear to miss their native meals of crayfish, frogs, small snakes, and swamp fish.

The meal over, do Bubbles and Tilly relax and stretch out for a snooze? No, they start in to *play*. They chase each other in the water, roll over and swim on their backs, dive, and go through all sorts of antics. They never seem to tire of having fun.

Once we built a slide for the otters. It was made so that they could slide down into the pool. But none of the otters we had at the time would use this slide. I could never understand it, and at other zoos I have found too that otters would not use slides which had been built for them.

But on the banks of streams and lakes, where otters live in the wild state, they seem never to grow weary of sliding down mud banks into the water. And in the winter they slide down the snow. They appear to have more fun coasting down these slides than at anything else they do. They reach the top of the slide, pull up their short legs, and go down on their bellies—much as boys go "belly-whopper" on their sleds. Only the otter's body is his sled.

But in zoos they simply will not use the slides built for them—and this remains a great mystery to me.

Bubbles and Tilly came to the Lincoln Park Zoo from Florida. They were caught quite young in the swamps where they lived.

Otters have a slender body which is from three and one-half to four and one-half feet long in the adults. They may weigh as much as twenty pounds. The tail is long and heavy, tapering to a point on the end. Their faces are rather flat and somewhat like those of pug dogs. They have short legs and there are webs between the toes. These webbed feet enable otters to swim very fast. Yet they can travel very well on land.

Otters belong to the weasel family. They have a valuable thick, brown fur, which consists of a soft undercoat with overlaying glossy guard hairs. This beautiful fur was highly prized by early trappers. Indians, too, valued this fur, and often magical qualities were attached to certain otter skins which were passed down for generations from father to son. The Plains Indians and some mountain tribes, such as the Utes, wore strips of otter skin around their wrists and on other parts of their bodies. Some braided the skin into their long hair and others twisted it into the scalp lock. The Arapaho Indians wore otter skin and thought it protected them from harm.

There is an interesting story about a certain kind of otter—the sea otter. This animal is larger and heavier than the fresh-water otter and sometimes weighs as much as eighty pounds.

46

The fur of the sea otter is of rare beauty, and because of this he was hunted years ago to such an extent that he almost completely disappeared. No more of these otters could be found in their usual habitat—off the California coast or among the Aleutian Islands, Alaska.

But just a few years ago some were located swimming off the coast of California. There was much excitement among nature lovers. The sea otter had made a comeback! A law was passed protecting them, and today they live peacefully again in the seaweed beds off the coasts of some of the Aleutian Islands and along the coast of southern California.

The sea otter often swims on his back. The mother otter carries her cub in this position. This is the way they eat, too—swimming on their backs and holding an abalone, crab, or sea urchin in their paws. They can even open oysters or clams while swimming on their backs. A clam is pressed down on the chest with one foot and hit with a rock held in the other.

Otters, such as Bubbles and Tilly, are much like happy, carefree children. They do not appear to have a worry on earth. Bubbles, especially, seems to be bubbling over with fun all the time. That is why we have named her Bubbles.

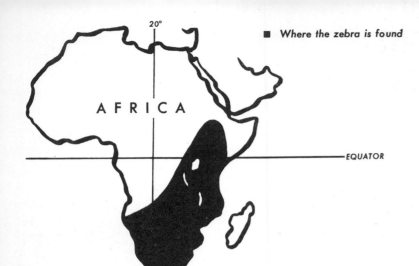

■ *Where the zebra is found*

AFRICA

EQUATOR

FRANK
the Zebra

VISITORS AT the Lincoln Park Zoo, when looking at Frank and Betty, the two Chapman's zebras, sometimes wonder: "Are these animals white with black stripes, or are they black with white stripes?"

That is a very old question, but a long time ago an answer was figured out by some smart fellow with a certain sense of humor: "Neither. They are invisible animals painted white and black."

There is another ancient puzzler we often hear: "What is black and white and red all over?"

Now that one is easy, you say. You've heard it before. The answer is—a newspaper.

No. The answer is—an embarrassed zebra!

And if any zebra could have been red all over with embarrassment, it would certainly have been our Frank on one occasion. For Frank, the male zebra, had a right to be put out after a tiff with Betty.

This happened one day when the two were together in their outdoor pen. The sun was as bright and the air as warm as it might have been on their native veldt in South Africa. They had just finished a good meal and were standing side by side, their positions reversed so that Frank could keep the flies off Betty's head with his tail, and Betty could do the same for Frank. They gave the impression of perfect contentment.

Then Frank became playful. He gave Betty a friendly nip on the rump. Betty wheeled to the side and let go with her heels. She kicked Frank smack in the face. It was not a playful kick, either—but a serious one. Apparently Betty meant to show that she would stand for no foolishness from a mere male.

When this zebra family spat was over, Frank's eye was black and blue. It had to be carefully dressed. For a time we were even afraid he might lose the sight in it. But his eye finally got well, and Frank and Betty have remained separated ever since.

This is what I mean by a zebra's being embarrassed—if such a thing could

actually happen. Frank, however, certainly appeared to be flustered by Betty's actions. . . .

Zebras are among the most popular of zoo animals. They look a great deal like donkeys with stripes, and because of this the old-time name for them was "tiger-ass." They are the African members of the horse family.

To settle the question asked in the beginning of my story, the body of the zebra is really white or cream in color. The stripes are black or brownish black.

In a zoo this type of coloring makes the zebra stand out distinctly from his background, and it is hard to imagine stripes as a protective coloring or camouflage in the animal's native surroundings. Yet there these dark stripes do serve this purpose, for at a distance they make it difficult for the eye to follow the outlines of the animal's body in the shadows of the forest or tall grass. Thus the zebra becomes almost invisible a few hundred yards away.

Like the horse or donkey, the zebra has a hoof on each foot. His tail is long and fleshy. At the end of the tail is a tuft of hair, much like that on the tail of a cow. The head and ears are much larger in proportion than those of a horse.

Zebras range in large herds, sometimes composed of hundreds of these animals. A young zebra will grow up and remain with the same herd to which its mother belonged.

They graze in company with giraffes, antelopes, and gnus. As they have unusually keen senses of smell, sight, and hearing, they are valuable to the other animals as sentinels and warn them of approaching danger. When they sense an enemy near, they snort loudly.

The lion is the zebra's worst enemy. Yet during the heat of the day zebras will often graze not far from lions that are dozing or sunning themselves. But after the sun goes down and the lions begin to stir, the zebras seek a safe place.

There are several kinds of zebras. The largest is called Grevy's zebra and is found in Africa from southern Ethiopia south to the Tana River. It is more horselike than other zebras and has more and narrower stripes. It is named for the man who first brought back a description of it from the plateaus of Ethiopia.

Grant's zebra, another type, is smaller than Grevy's zebra and is to be found on the highland plains of South Africa. It has the broadest markings of all zebras. Most zebras in zoos are of this race.

Chapman's zebra is at home from Bechuanaland north to the Sudan, and today is the most common. The South African dauw (pronounced like "cow"), or Burchell's zebra, is still another. Its body and belly are striped but the legs are plain or nearly so. It is rare today, but can be found in some zoos.

The mountain zebra is the smallest of them all. A native of the mountains in South Africa, this zebra is almost extinct. Its body and legs are striped but the belly is plain.

Not so many years ago there was a zebra-like animal known as the quagga. The head, shoulders, and forepart of its body were striped, but the back part and legs were plain and its ears quite small. But the quagga is now extinct.

Zebras in their wild state live on grass. They also eat the tender leaves of trees, sometimes standing erect on their hind legs in order to reach them.

But Frank and Betty thrive on oats, whole-wheat bread, hay, carrots, apples, and lettuce. Until Frank gets over his embarrassment and Betty calms down and learns to control her heels, we will see that they dine apart, each in his own yard.

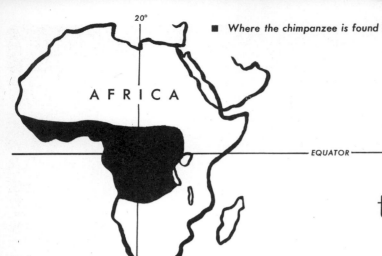

AFRICA

20°

EQUATOR

HEINIE II
the Chimpanzee

A BATH EVERY DAY, you say! . . . You wash him in warm water with a sponge, and he likes it? Well, he does look clean, and happy."

The visitor glanced again at Heinie II, who was looking right back at him. Then Heinie II seemed to give an indifferent shrug. He turned away and picked up an automobile tire, rolled it around in a small circle, jumped up on a shelf, and then hopped down to catch the tire before it stopped rolling.

Yes, Heinie II did look clean and sleek, and he most certainly was happy and contented. But there was something else about Heinie II that aroused the visitor's interest. It almost looked as if the young chimpanzee was listening to everything that was said, and not only listening but understanding it.

The keeper went toward the cage and began to make a strange sound: "Ou-ou-ou! Ou-ou-ou!"

Heinie II replied with the same deep guttural: "Ou-ou-ou! Ou-ou-ou!"

The keeper reached in and began to tickle Heinie II in the ribs. The chimpanzee rolled over on his back and continued to make the same noise, much as if he were laughing.

"That's chimp talk," explained the keeper. "I go 'ou-ou-ou!' to him, and he answers. It is a friendly greeting and a sort of laugh, too. As you see, he keeps doing it when I tickle him."

"You mean you can talk in his own language?" asked the surprised visitor.

"Well, if you want to call it a language. Certain sounds show their feelings. But, of course, chimps cannot talk. They bark or scream when they are angry or frightened. They make this 'ou-ou-ou' sound when they are happy. Some people say chimps use as many as twenty different sounds to express themselves."

Chimpanzees, like Heinie II, are often thought to be the most intelligent of the manlike apes. They are probably more like human beings than any other animal. Their vocal cords are like the human, too, and they could actually talk if it were not for the fact that the part of the brain which controls speech is not fully developed in them.

Even if they don't talk—yet some trainers have claimed chimps could learn one word and repeat it clearly—they have ways of making their feelings known. In addition to sounds, they have telling facial expressions and bodily gestures. For instance, when a chimpanzee does not like anything, he turns and walks away. This is a meaningful gesture, and he makes it in a way that is just as plain as if he said: "I won't have anything to do with that thing."

Heinie II was less than a year old when he arrived at the Lincoln Park Zoo on December 9, 1949. He had traveled by boat from Africa to New York. I brought him to Chicago from New York on a passenger plane at the same time I brought Ling Wong, the orangutan. Heinie II and Ling Wong have been pals ever since. They live in adjoining cages and often are allowed to play together.

Careful feeding and the daily sponge baths have kept Heinie II healthy and contented. He learns quickly. He likes to be dressed up in clothes and ride a tricycle. He watches people closely and then imitates their actions. And how he enjoys an audience!

Training a bright young chimpanzee like Heinie II is fun. The first thing he must learn is to obey. When he is told to do something and does not do it, his trainer says "AH-ah!" and shakes his head and wags his finger at him. Heinie II understands and tries to do better next time. If he is told to sit still in a chair, he will do it. If he gets fidgety, the trainer says "AH-ah!" again and wags his finger, and Heinie II remains quiet.

Heinie II is the namesake of thirty-two-year-old Heinie, who has been in our zoo since 1924. Heinie the elder is old for a chimpanzee but is still in good health. He has long been an attraction in the Monkey House, especially when he puts on his "wild man" act. He goes into tantrums, kicks the door of his cage, stomps on the floor, and glares out at everyone.

Chimpanzees are the most abundant of the great apes. They are smaller than the gorilla and the orangutan, but can make a lot more noise. In the jungle at night their loud cry can be heard a mile away.

They live in equatorial Africa from the Atlantic Ocean to the Nile River. Much of their time is spent in trees, and their main food is fruit. They range the forests in large family groups consisting of a male and several females and their young ones. Sometimes the group may contain from twenty to thirty larger chimps. They are quite affectionate, and pet and fondle one another to show affection as humans do.

The male chimpanzee may grow as large as five feet tall and weigh as much as 160 pounds. In captivity chimps live to be thirty-five to forty years old. They can stand and walk erect but prefer to lean on their long, powerful arms.

54

Because of their intelligence, ability to learn, and remember things taught them, chimpanzees have long been of interest to scientists. In studying them scientists believe they can learn why human beings sometimes act the way they do. They think the chimpanzee behaves much as early man did.

Like other well-trained chimpanzees, Heinie II will learn many more tricks. But we would like to keep him as natural as possible. He is just as interesting—maybe more so—as an unspoiled chimp. I must say I like him better when he is himself than when he is dressed up in clothes and trying to act like a human.

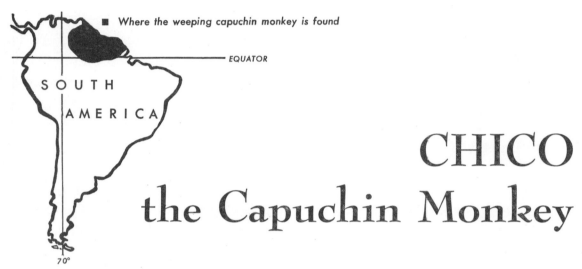

■ *Where the weeping capuchin monkey is found*

EQUATOR

SOUTH

AMERICA

70°

CHICO
the Capuchin Monkey

Imagine Chico dressed in an embroidered bolero jacket, velvet trousers, and a cocky fez on his head, carrying a cup for pennies and dancing at the end of a chain to the strains of "*O Sole Mio.*"

If things had turned out differently for our monkey friend Chico, he might have been seen thus on the city streets with his master, one "Signor Giuseppe Garibaldi," about the time the first crocus peeped through the damp earth and the buds began to appear on the tips of the tree branches. Seeing Chico and his organ-grinder master, everyone would know that spring had come at last.

Today, alas, we seldom see a Chico or a "Giuseppe" or a grind organ on the city streets. They have become almost as rare as the horse and buggy, the iceman and his wagon, or the cigar-store wooden Indian of a bygone time.

But Chico, the little capuchin monkey—the kind of monkey we ordinarily see with organ grinders and in circuses—is far more important in the zoo. For there he is a star in his own right. He is the major attraction at the Children's Zoo in Chicago's Lincoln Park. He is known as a "capuchin" monkey because

the hair on top of his head looks like the cap or hood worn by the Capuchin monk.

Chico does many more acts in the Children's Zoo to delight the youngsters than he ever would have done had he been trained at the end of an organ-grinder's chain. He is mischievous and full of fun. He leaps up on high boxes and makes faces. He plays pranks and imitates people. He is a born mimic.

Sometimes Chico will make a leap and land on his trainer's shoulder. Then he will curl his long tail around the trainer's neck and wrap his own arms and legs around one of the trainer's arms. His head will be down. He likes to see how the world looks upside down. Maybe it makes better sense to him that way!

Chico goes into one of his funniest acts when someone gives him a pinch of tobacco. Don't worry, he has more sense than to put it into his mouth. But the smell of it appears to excite him. He will rub it on all parts of his body, especially on his long tail. He acts much like a cat with a catnip ball.

Chico also is a television star. He has appeared on several programs and always has managed to steal the show. One of his most successful appearances was on the Quiz Kids program. This was one time when he seemed to try to behave himself and look wise. But in doing this he was funnier than ever.

Chico, who comes from South America, is a type of monkey known as a "weeper." Such monkeys make a sound which resembles that of a child weeping. It is a plaintive little call. But do not be misled and imagine because of this call that Chico or any other "weeper" is sad! For immediately after "weeping" he will be playing some mischievous trick.

There is never a dull moment in a cage full of capuchin monkeys—or in a cage full of any type of monkeys, for that matter. They leap, chatter, weep, howl, and screech, tease one another, and go through all sorts of antics. And there are always crowds of visitors at their cage, laughing and applauding them.

There are more kinds of monkeys than you can shake a banana at. Some are smaller than cats and others larger than dogs. They have a large variety of tails—curly tails, straight tails, bushy tails, and stub tails. Some have no tails at all. There are monkeys with hair on their faces and others whose faces are naked. There are dog-faced monkeys and purple-faced monkeys, some with white cheeks, others with turned-up noses, and still others with tufted ears or whiskers. Some monkeys appear to be wearing mufflers around their necks, and others appear to have on toupees.

Mustached guenon

Monkeys are divided into two general groups—Old World monkeys and New World monkeys. The main difference between these two types is that some of those from the New World—the tropical regions of South and Central

America—have long tails which they can wrap around trees and branches and by which they can hang. Such tails are called "prehensile" tails. The New World monkeys include the howler monkey, whose name is taken from his howling cry, the spider monkey, the capuchin, and the woolly monkey, whose fur is very thick and woolly-looking.

Pig-tailed macaque

The Old World types do not have the prehensile tail. Some have only short tails, and others are like the apes and have no tails. There are many more different kinds of Old World monkeys than there are of New World monkeys. They include the baboon, a large dog-faced monkey found in Arabia and Africa; the pig-tailed monkey of the Malay Peninsula that is trained by the natives to climb coconut trees and throw down the fruit; the sacred hanuman monkey of India that travels freely in groups about the villages, eating the natives' grain and fruit; the long-nosed monkey of Borneo, whose nose is very long and beaklike; and the green monkey of Africa, whose fur is dark green and black.

Monkeys are social creatures and live in family groups. They spend the greater part of their lives in trees. The capuchin, for instance, has four "hands," not two, and seldom walks on the ground. His feet are almost the same shape as his hands, and the big toe on his foot looks like a thumb.

Mandrill

If you are standing before a cage, feeding monkeys peanuts, and you notice one of them stuffing nuts in his cheeks, you will know at once that he is an Old World monkey. Such monkeys have cheek pouches where they can store food. New World monkeys have no such pouches.

At the zoo you will often see one monkey carefully examining the hair on the back of another. He will part the hair with his fingers, pick off something, and place it in his mouth and eat it. Some people think he does this because he likes salt and what he picks off is a small flake of skin which has a salty taste. I, myself, think the action is really a grooming one, by which monkeys keep one another neat and clean.

Lar gibbon

Monkeys in captivity are fed fruits, vegetables, and whole-wheat bread, and are given multiple vitamins to keep them healthy. Since in the wild state they eat insects, at our zoo we also feed them meal worms. In order to do this we raise our own meal worms. Chico and all his fellow monkeys find the worms a special treat.

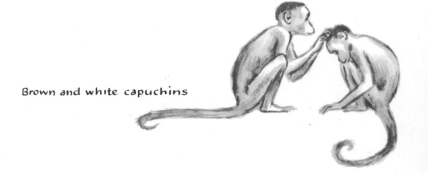

Brown and white capuchins

NOAH
the Camel

AWAY BACK before recorded history, camels had already been tamed. They were used for carrying heavy loads, for riding, and for pulling the plow. They were domesticated so long ago that there are no man-made records.

They have always been with man, like the horse and the dog and the cat, and the only so-called wild camels were ones that had wandered off or been turned loose, and had become untractable like the mustangs of our western and southwestern plains. . . .

Which brings us to the strange story of Noah. Noah is a huge bull camel with two humps. He is known as a Bactrian camel—the kind found in Asia. But Noah did not come from Asia. He came from the zoo in Columbus, Ohio, where he was born.

Considering the fact that camels have been domesticated for so long a time, it would seem that Noah would be a gentle, peaceable, and mild-mannered animal. But no. Despite all the kindness and attention given him since birth, and despite his not having to work and carry heavy loads across the desert wastes— or never having an opportunity to run loose—Noah has become a wild and unruly animal.

He appears gentle enough when he comes up toward you in his outdoor yard in the Lincoln Park Zoo. But do not be misled. Noah will take a savage nip at anyone who gets too near.

Perhaps it might be just as well to call him temperamental. That is a trait to be found in all camels—even those called tame—and their masters have to be on guard at all times. However, I would say that Noah is much worse than most. He is a good example of what a camel was like in the wild stage in Asia long before man learned to tame him.

Something evidently happened to Noah to spoil his disposition. It might have been that, in his young days as a baby camel, he was teased by visitors, or it might have been the ride in a truck from Columbus to Chicago on a cold, blustery, December day.

During that ride they ran into a blizzard. Noah was in a crate on the truck and, to keep the wind off him, a tarpaulin was spread over the crate. Camels can stand extreme temperatures, hot or cold, and Noah did not seem to mind the blizzard too much. But he had been used to the comforts of zoo life and might have resented what he thought was ill-treatment.

When he arrived at the Lincoln Park Zoo, he was about nine months old and weighed 1,000 pounds. He showed his surly disposition right from the start and grew wilder as the years went by. Now at seven years of age and weighing some 2,000 pounds, he is an obstreperous camel.

Noah usually is up to some mischief, too. He is either biting at the lock and chain on the gate to his enclosure, trying to break it open, or endeavoring to loosen the wire on his fence.

The oddest thing about a camel is the hump on his back. These humps have no bony structure. If the camel had disappeared from the earth before man began to write history, and bones later had been found, there would have been no way to reconstruct a camel exactly as he looks. The men who reconstruct early animals, and have rebuilt, so to speak, dinosaurs and other prehistoric creatures, certainly would have no way of knowing that the camel had a hump or humps.

The camel with one hump is known as the true or Arabian camel—or the dromedary. The two-humped camel is the Bactrian camel.

The dromedary, or one-humped camel, is more widespread than the Bactrian, or two-humped camel. The dromedary is found in northern Africa—especially in the Sahara Desert—Egypt, southwestern Asia, and Arabia.

Arabian camel

Among the dromedary camels there are different breeds, just as in horses. Some, the white ones, are fast and comfortable for riding. They are called "riding camels," and can travel at the rate of ten miles an hour and carry a rider on the average of one hundred miles a day. The Arabs own the finest of these camels. Their white riding camels are pure-blooded and pedigreed.

Bactrian camel

Other dromedary camels are called "baggage camels" and are slow, rough-riding, and more cumbersome in their actions. It is considered bad etiquette for an Arabian gentleman to be mounted on such a camel. Something like a cowboy mounted on a mule!

Dromedaries have been introduced into Australia, Spain, and Zanzibar. In 1856 they were brought to the United States to be used in the desert regions, but the experiment was soon abandoned. However, ten years later, another attempt was made to breed them in Texas and Arizona, but this also was given up. For years many of these animals ran wild on our western deserts.

Two-humped, or Bactrian, camels are used in Asia as far north as Siberia. They are often loaded with as much as 1,000 pounds and with this load can travel at a steady pace from two and a half to three miles an hour.

The camel can go as long as ten days without water, and as the oases, or watering places, in the deserts are about nine days' journey apart, if the camel is on the right road he does not suffer from thirst. His feet are protected by thick and broad sole pads which keep him from sinking into the sand. His slit nostrils can be closed against flying dust, and his eyes are protected by long lashes. He is fitted by Nature to be the ideal "ship of the desert."

Camels can eat almost any kind of food. In the desert they can bite off and eat even the thorny plants that grow there.

Noah, however, has never had to eat such food. He has the best of alfalfa hay, oats, raw carrots, and whole-wheat bread. When he is well fed, the two humps on his back are filled out. When he does not eat, the fat in these humps is absorbed by his body for food and the humps become flabby.

Strange as it may seem, Noah fasts during Lent. Just about the time Lent comes around, he will cut down on his food and consume only about one-third of it. He will not start eating regular meals until after Easter.

It is impossible for Noah to know it is the Lenten season—it just happens that this is the time of year for him to cut down on his food. It would be too much to expect that a camel with Noah's surly disposition could in any way be pious!

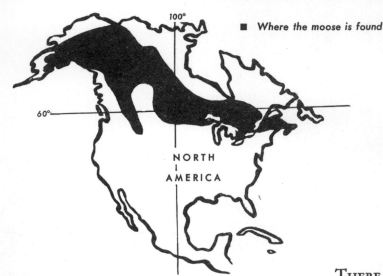

MOUSSANCE the Moose

THERE WAS a profound silence in the banquet hall. The master of ceremonies had announced that he had a surprise guest—perhaps two surprise guests. The sportsmen at the banquet looked around at one another. No guest or guests were appearing.

Then they heard some strange noises and a clatter of feet which seemed to come from outside the entrance. The doors swung open and a head appeared.

And what a head! It was the kind that many of them had mounted as trophies on the walls of their dens—only this one did not have large antlers. It was the head of a moose. The moose stood in the door and looked calmly in at the assembled diners.

"Moussance the Moose!" introduced the master of ceremonies. The sportsmen, once over their surprise, began to cheer.

Moussance walked into the banquet hall. Then right behind her came another moose.

"Ontie the Moose!" called the master of ceremonies. More cheers.

When the two moose had casually sauntered into the banquet hall, as if it were not unusual for moose to make calls on the eighth floor of a hotel, they were followed by a big, heavy-set man with a full beard, who was dressed in rough clothes.

"Joe LaFlamme, the Canadian trapper!"

Joe waved a greeting with one hand. In the other he had two ropes which were attached to halters on Moussance and Ontie. The banquet hall was now in an uproar.

Some of the guests began to make moose calls, which sounded like "Who-are-you? Who-are-you?" But which actually were more like this: "Moo-waugh-yuh? Moo-waugh-yuh?"

It was the female moose call. Others imitated the male, or bull moose: "Oh-ah, oh-ah, oh-ah! Oh-ah, oh-ah, oh-ah!"

These calls, however, had no effect on Moussance and Ontie. They were too busy nibbling the lettuce and bread given them by their many admirers. They were having a fine time at the banquet. And Joe, the Canadian trapper, was busy answering questions as to how he had ever trained two moose that were as gentle as pet cows on a farm.

Joe told how he had caught them in the forests of Ontario when they were very young. And he had just trained them! He had made a harness for each and could hitch both to a sled. He had shown them at Sportsmen's Shows all over the east, and now Buffalo was his last stop. He was going back to his home in Ontario.

But Joe did not take Moussance and Ontie with him. I saw to that. There are few moose in captivity, and I wanted these for the Buffalo Zoo, of which I was then the curator.

So Moussance and her friend were placed in the zoo. Moussance was one of the biggest moose I ever saw. She was higher at the shoulders than a tall man. In fact, she measured six feet two inches.

We fed Moussance and Ontie on cut branches of poplar, willow, birch, and aspen trees. They could chew up a small limb as big around as a pencil. We also gave them prepared food in pellet form, as well as crushed oats, bran, and alfalfa hay.

In the summer we found they were bothered by deer flies. So we built a special "moose shower bath." This shower had water coming out on both sides and Moussance and Ontie would walk between the sprays and get rid of their flies. We had a mud pond where they could roll. It made them feel good to roll in the mud and this kept off the flies, too.

Moose are the largest deer in the world. They are still to be found in the same regions where they have always lived—the large forests of Nova Scotia, New Brunswick, Maine, Quebec, Ontario, Manitoba, and northern Minnesota. Then, where the prairies begin, there are no moose, but farther northwest they are found in British Columbia, up into Alaska, and down into Yellowstone Park and other mountain areas in the northern Rocky Mountain states. In Alaska they grow the biggest.

The Algonquin Indians called them "moos," and that is where the name came from. The moose was as important to the Woodland Indians as the buffalo (or bison) was to the Plains Indians. The moose provided these Indians with food and clothing.

Moose are perhaps the least graceful of the deer family. They are awkward-looking animals with huge bodies, spindling legs, large heads, bulky rounded muzzles or noses, and large ears. They have a hump over the withers, or

shoulders, and thin hindquarters. The hair is blackish brown except for gray on the legs. Both the male and the female have a tail-like piece of skin dangling from the throat. This is called a "bell," and is usually about eight inches long, but in some moose it grows to be a foot or more long. It disappears when the moose reaches old age.

Most people think of the moose as an animal with huge, shovel-like antlers. Only the bull moose has these antlers, and they begin to sprout at the coming of warm weather. They are first covered with what is called "velvet," a sort of downy covering. This velvet is rubbed off in strips at the end of September when the antlers are fully grown. The antlers are carried through the fall and winter, and when they drop off in February or March, the new ones start growing immediately.

The antlers are the fighting weapons. They are of solid bone, and big ones measure almost six feet from tip to tip, or as wide as a man is tall. It is when the velvet comes off the antlers that bull moose challenge each other in the forests. They bellow so loud they can be heard for four miles or more.

When bull moose fight, they tear up the ground and shrubbery on their battlefield, and the clash of their antlers makes a terrific noise. The winner of the fight is soon joined by the cow moose, while the loser slinks off alone. Although bull moose use their antlers in such fights among themselves, when engaged against other animals they employ their front feet to stamp the life out of their enemies. Despite the size of a bull moose's antlers he can run with ease through dense forests without getting caught on branches. He holds his antlers back on his withers and the branches just slide off.

When the snow is deep, several moose will meet and make what is called a "moose yard." They trample down paths back and forth through the thickets or swamps at a place where they expect to spend the winter—a place where there is plenty of food. This is the time of year that moose meet together or appear sociable. At most other times they travel alone.

The moose is a browsing animal and lives on twigs, barks, and the buds of bushes in the fall and winter months. A moose will straddle a sapling with his forelegs, bend it down, and chew off the tender ends. In the summer they like leaves and "pads," or stems, of the water lily and other juicy plants. They are excellent swimmers.

I have often wondered if Joe, the Canadian trapper, has tamed other moose. At any other Sportsmen's Show banquet I would not be surprised to see the head of a big moose like Moussance appear suddenly in the door of the banquet hall. I would be pleased, for right now we need a moose at the zoo.

64

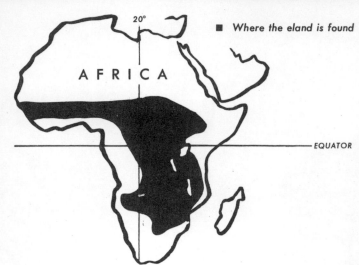

AFRICA

20°

EQUATOR

LEAR
the Eland

LEAR LOST NO TIME as a baby in becoming a full-grown eland. That is, as far as his food was concerned.

Nearly all young animals are dependent on their mothers for their food—at least for the first few weeks. But not Lear. He was just a few days old when he nudged his way to his mother's feed bin and helped himself to the grain. Soon he was eating hay.

If we at Lincoln Park Zoo had not raised other baby elands, we might have been very much surprised. But we had seen this happen before.

There was one eland fawn, for example, who began eating just a few hours after he was born. He could not even stand on his feet yet and was lying down. Leaves were blowing off the poplar trees near by and, when one came close to this greedy little fellow, he turned his head and grabbed the leaf in his mouth and began eating it.

When you have been around animals for a long time, this will, of course, strike you as unusual. But elands for some reason develop very quickly. Possibly it is Nature's way of protecting them. They are continually on the run from their enemies so they cannot remain babies for long—they have to be able to dart away with the herd.

Lear was no exception to this rapid growth, and it was not long before he was capable of taking care of himself. He was named after Lear Grimmer, Assistant Director, and is the fourth eland fawn born to George and Ida at Lincoln Park. The parents were born in captivity. Ida has been a good mother, kind and gentle and very considerate. She never appears to resent the fact that her young ones want to grow up fast, right from birth, and be independent.

Lear's little horns began to grow straight out of his head in a corkscrew fashion, which is a peculiarity of eland horns. When fully developed, they stick straight back and up and have spiral grooves in them. Elands belong to the antelope family, and usually only the male antelopes have horns. But both male and female elands grow horns. These horns are hollow—like those of cattle,

66

sheep, and goats—and the elands do not shed them as the members of the deer family shed their antlers, which are of solid bone. The eland's horns, like those of all true antelopes, are without branches.

There are some eighty species of antelopes. Most of them are to be found in Africa, although some may be found in Asia, India, and Russia.

They vary in size from the eland, which is the size of a horse and is the largest of the species, to the pygmy antelope of Africa, which is only thirteen inches high at the shoulders. Antelopes live on the plains, in forests, or mountains, but several species, including the reedbuck, live in swamps.

I shall not try to describe all the kinds, but there are many of them, some with very odd names—the bushbuck, waterbuck, marshbuck, impala, kudu, bongo (large forest antelope), dik-dik (small antelope, the size of a hare), klipspringer, steenbok, addax, nilgai, duiker or diving buck, so-called from its habit of diving suddenly into the bush, and the odd-looking gnus, to give some examples.

The gnus are large oxlike animals native to Africa. Both sexes have horns that curve down and outward, the head is somewhat broad, tufts of hair stand erect on the muzzle, and long hair hangs from the throat between the forelegs.

Pronghorn antelope

The so-called pronghorn is the only antelope in the United States. There are some who claim that the pronghorn is not a true antelope because it sheds its horns each season and because each horn has a prong on the forward edge, which gives the animal its name. So it is usually considered as being of a separate family.

However, the pronghorn is an interesting animal. It lives on the western plains and dry plateaus and is very nimble and swift. Pronghorns are sociable, playful creatures and live together in herds of from six to thirty. They are timid and wary and, when grazing, they keep a sharp lookout at all times for enemies.

Since all types of antelopes have long been valued as food and for their skins and horns, many have almost become extinct. This is true in America as well as in Africa. Laws now protect them in the United States, and in Africa many are protected in Kruger National Park, Transvaal, and other preserves.

Like deer and cattle, antelopes are ruminants and are herbivorous. This means that they chew their cuds and live off grasses and other vegetable matter.

Lear and his parents now are fed grain and hay, raw carrots, and whole-wheat bread. It may not be long before Lear has a brother or sister eland, and it will be interesting to see how quickly this one learns to eat grown-up eland food.

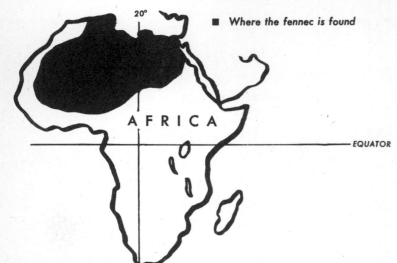

20°

AFRICA

EQUATOR

FUAD
the Fennec

ON CERTAIN AFTERNOONS Fuad the fennec is taken from his cage for a romp. His playroom is just behind the cage of Judy the elephant, in the office of Keeper Paul Dittambl.

Paul tosses a small rubber ball to Fuad, who begins chasing it around the room. He plays with it as a dog would, grabbing it in his mouth and tossing his head, then letting the ball go in such a way that it flies through the air. He is right after it. He will not retrieve, or bring back the ball, as dogs often do, but Paul says he would undoubtedly do this if an effort were made to train him.

Fuad is a quick little fellow, as quick as a fox—which is not unnatural because he *is* a fox. A desert fox.

As Fuad plays, he makes a peculiar whining sound, not unlike that made by a dog. He barks, too, and it sounds like *yak-yak-yak-yak*, a typically doglike bark, only in a higher note. Like a dog, he also wants attention. He will scurry around the room and then suddenly stop in front of Paul, turning over on his back with his feet in the air. He wants his belly rubbed.

In their natural state fennecs—or, as some call them, desert zerdas—are wild little creatures. But apparently Fuad was caught while very young and raised in a family where he was treated kindly. He is now quite tame.

His mate, Fatima, is not so tame. She is sometimes called a vixen, which really is the right way to speak of her, as vixen means female fox. However, she is also a vixen in the way the word is sometimes used, in the sense of a shrewish, ill-tempered being. Fatima will sometimes bark and snap at Paul when he tries to pick her up. But once she has been picked up and seems to realize that no harm will come to her, she is gentle and responds to attention.

Both Fuad and Fatima were bought from a dealer in North Africa. It is believed that they originally came from Egypt, from the edge of the Sahara Desert. They are tiny creatures as foxes go and are the smallest members of the fox family.

Fuad weighs a little more than two pounds. He looks much larger because

of his thick fur. This fur is soft and almost like down. It is a fawn color, much the same color as the sands of the desert. The color of Fuad's coat is another example of Nature's way of giving protective colors to animals—colors which enable them to blend in with their surroundings. Fuad's coat is slightly darker in color than that of his mate, Fatima.

Fennecs generally are about as long as a foot ruler, and their tails just a little more than half that size. But the fennec's tail is large and bushy, like that of other foxes.

The most striking feature of the fennec, besides his small size, is his enormous ears. They are very large and pointed. Fennecs have been given such ears so that they can pick up the slightest sounds on the desert sands. Sand tends to deaden sound, and animals can move much more quietly in sand, as the sound does not carry far. With his large ears the fennec can pick up the tiniest noise. He can hear a mouse, a lizard, or an insect moving at some distance from him, and this is very important to him because he lives mainly on such foods.

Fennecs and other foxes belong to the dog family. They resemble dogs, just as wolves do, and have many doglike features. For instance, the fennec has teeth very similar to those of a dog.

The baby fennec is called a pup, too. He is born in a snug hole, or burrow, which his parents make under the shelter of a desert shrub, or clump of desert grass, or some overhanging rock. When digging a hole under a clump of grass, the fennec is careful not to break or cut the long roots which extend deep down into the earth. He pushes them aside, and they serve as a foundation structure to prevent a cave-in of the burrow. The dens are lined with leaves, hair, and feathers of the ostrich or other birds.

Fennecs seldom go out during the heat of the day. They appear around dusk, at which time they begin their search for food. It is usually hard to see them. As they move about, they trot down into the hollows and skirt the rocks leading into ravines.

There is a surprising variety of food to be found in the desert. Besides insects, mice, and lizards, fennecs enjoy a meal of a certain queer type of snail which they find by digging among the roots of the desert grasses. They also like ripe dates, figs, melons, and wild grapes.

Fuad and Fatima have a sweet tooth, too. They like bananas and parboiled sweet potatoes. We peel the potatoes for them and cut them up and place them in a small dish in their cage. They also are fed chopped raw meat.

Visitors usually see Fuad and Fatima curled up comfortably in their cages, sleeping. But Fuad at the present time has been more awake during the day than usual. He can be seen at the back of his cage, sniffing curiously, his ears pointed to catch any sound.

He knows that in a small cage, just in back, there is another fennec, recently obtained by the Lincoln Park Zoo from the zoo in Columbus, Ohio. Fuad is particularly interested because it is a female fennec whose name is Farida.

Fatima does not appear to be jealous. Perhaps she is just shamming, and actually her sharp, pointed, little nose is just a bit out of joint at the thought of a rival. Or she may be consoling herself with the thought that she is presenting some new fennec pups to the zoo one of these days.

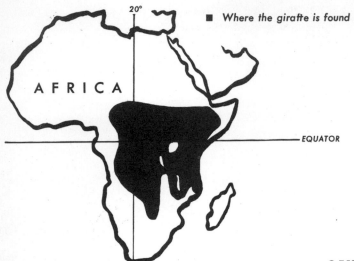

AFRICA

20°

EQUATOR

JUNIOR
the Giraffe

QUIET, PLEASE. GIRAFFES ARE NERVOUS AND EXCITABLE. The sign seems out of place as Junior lies peacefully in his cage, chewing his cud as a cow does, his large, friendly eyes peering out from under long lashes. There are all sorts of noise in front of his cage—shuffling of feet, laughter, and conversation—but he appears happy and contented.

Still, Junior's small ears are ready to catch any strange sound. Should that small boy's balloon suddenly burst, or this woman's picnic basket drop with a clatter of dishes, Junior would be on his feet in an instant and might start running around his cage in fright. He might be joined by Virginia, who is in the same cage, and the keepers would have a hard time quieting the two animals.

That is the reason for the sign. It does not mean that Junior might hurt someone if he became frightened—but that he might hurt himself. Giraffes are valuable animals, and great care must be taken to safeguard them.

Junior is one of four giraffes at the Brookfield Zoo. He was born in the zoo at Columbus, Ohio, and brought to Chicago when thirteen months old. He is now two years old and the only male giraffe at Brookfield.

Junior and his three companions are what are known as "reticulated" giraffes because of the netlike pattern of their markings. But in general appearance they are like other giraffes.

Many consider giraffes among the most interesting animals in captivity. The very long necks of these animals make them the tallest of all members of the animal kingdom. The heads of some grown giraffes are as high as eighteen feet from the ground. Animals this tall could nibble leaves from plants in a flower box in a second-story window. Their long, ten-inch tongues would help to make this easy.

People always want to know why giraffes have such long necks. If they are told that this neck was given giraffes by Nature so they could eat the leaves and small branches of the acacias, mimosas, and other trees in Africa south of the Sahara Desert, where giraffes live in a wild state, this brings up another idea. Is it

QUIET,

not *because* of their long necks that they are able to eat leaves from tall trees? With that we are back where we started. . . .

But the giraffe's long and graceful neck, even if it cannot be explained, is the thing that makes the animal so popular. It is even more interesting when one learns that a giraffe has only seven bones in his neck, the same number as in a human being's neck. The little sparrow has fourteen bones in his small, short neck!

Food travels a long way down a giraffe's neck. He eats slowly and daintily, and swallows his food in little balls. When he has more time, he brings these balls back up, one by one, with an undignified belch, and chews them thoroughly. So his food actually makes three trips up and down his neck before he swallows it for good.

The giraffe, living in a country where there are dry seasons, can go three or more days without a drink of water. But the dew on young leaves eaten early in the morning helps to quench his thirst.

There are other odd things about giraffes. Their bodies look like camels in shape and leopards in color. So the old name for them was camelopards.

The giraffe's color is a reddish brown and white. The markings form a leaf-like pattern. Nature has marked him thus so that when standing amidst trees he is hard to distinguish at a distance. He just melts into the background.

At first glance it would appear that a giraffe's hind legs are shorter than his forelegs. But the length of both hind legs and forelegs is the same. The slope of his shoulders and his long neck give the illusion of longer forelegs.

Also, the giraffe appears to run in a stiff-legged fashion. He is a pacing animal. However, he does bend his legs, just as a horse does.

His powerful forelegs, ending in sharp hoofs, are the giraffe's fighting weapons. A giraffe can stand off animals as strong as lions and leopards by striking at them with his forefeet..

While the giraffe feeds mostly on trees, he can reach down and nibble grass. But he must spread his forelegs wide apart to lower his head. This is the way he drinks water, too.

Two small horns stick out on top of the giraffe's head. The giraffe found farthest north has a third horn in the middle of the forehead. The horns are covered with skin and hair and are used at times to fight with. If they are broken off, the giraffe may die.

His eyes are large and set wide apart. Behind each eye is a deep groove so that, by rolling his eyes backward without turning his head, the giraffe can see anything approaching him from the rear.

For a long time it was thought that giraffes were mute, that they could not utter a sound. But young calves, when hungry or when away from their mothers, bleat just like lambs. Older giraffes, too, have been heard to make noises like low growls when things did not suit them.

In their wild state giraffes travel in herds. They associate with zebras and gnus. Zebras are valuable friends because, while grazing, one or more of their number act as a lookout and bark a warning when they see an enemy.

For some years no giraffes were brought into the United States because of the law prohibiting the importation of certain animals which are subject to the hoof-and-mouth disease. In 1953 this law was modified, so that some giraffes may be imported now.

But giraffes in captivity bear young ones and they are easily raised. Some live to the ripe old age of thirty years. They get good food and seem to like their soybean greens and alfalfa hay as much as their native foods. Then, too, they are given endive, chard, a light grain mash, chopped roots, and fruits.

As soon as Junior has had a few years more of this fine food, it is hoped he will become a father and there will be other little Juniors at the Brookfield Zoo.

BUSTER
the Sea Lion

BUSTER GIVES a couple of loud, hoarse barks and slides into the water. He begins swimming in a circle, shooting through the water faster than most fish can. Every now and then his head comes up, and he gives another bark.

Betty slides into the water right after him. As he circles around, she is right behind. Around and around they go, swimming with such grace and ease that there is hardly a ripple on the surface of the water.

Sea lions, like otters and some other animals, appear to be happy and full of fun most of the time. They like to play. They seem just as contented in captivity as in their native ocean. For the rocky coasts of the ocean are their real home.

The first question that comes to mind is: Do Buster and Betty have salt water in their pool at the zoo? The answer is yes—and here is how we manage it: At the beginning of the week the water in their pool is fresh. Into this is dumped one hundred pounds of salt. When the salt is dissolved, the water in the pool is just about as salty as sea water. For a day the water in the pool is still—that is, no water is run into it—and the sea lions play around in water much like that they would find in their native ocean.

After the first day, the tap is opened and fresh water is allowed to flow gently into the pool. By the end of the week the salt water is so diluted that it is only brackish. The sea lions are then swimming in water which is nearly sweet, or fresh. Then, salt is added once more. This process is repeated week after week.

Sea lions spend only part of their time in the water. This is why they are called amphibious animals. This means that they live both in water and on land. I will have more to say about this later, but now I should like to tell something about Buster's history.

This will be the story of his experience when he was about a year old. His adventure is much like that of many other sea lions found in zoos—that is, those sea lions who were not born in captivity.

Buster was born on Santa Cruz Island, which is just off the coast of California.

It is here that sea lions live at certain seasons of the year in the caves or rookeries which form their breeding grounds.

Like other sea lions, Buster, when young, could do little for himself. His mother had to show him how to swim and how to catch fish. After a time he learned to play. He would "follow the leader," sliding off the rocks into the sea and chasing the other young lions. In a sort of "ball game" the sea lions would toss seaweed up in the air and catch it on their noses.

Then one night, when Buster and other members of his family had gone into their cave to sleep, some men came in a boat and stretched a net across the entrance of the cave. It was one of the caves that was entered from the water.

The next morning, when all the family had slipped into the water and started to swim out of the cave, they were caught in the net. The men, however, took only the young ones. Buster was one of these.

Buster was placed in a crate at once. He was taken to Santa Barbara and finally sent to the Lincoln Park Zoo at Chicago. During all this time he was not fed. Sea lions can go for as long as seven days without food, and when they are shipped from place to place they are never fed. This is to keep them from becoming sick on their journey.

Buster arrived at the zoo with a good appetite. He was none the worse for his trip. When placed in the pool in the basement of the Reptile House, he seemed right at home. He had a companion in Betty, who had been brought to the zoo at the same time.

Sea lions are protected by law, and it is necessary to have a permit to catch them. Such a permit can be obtained only in case a zoo wants a sea lion. Experts are sent out to capture them, and every precaution is taken to keep the animals from being harmed in any way.

Now, about the matter of sea lions living on both land and water. Once, like all living creatures, sea lions came from out of the sea and learned to live on land. They lived on land a long time and gradually found it unnecessary to return to the water.

But the strange thing is this. After living on land for a long time, the sea lions finally went back again to the water. They did not return to living entirely in the water, but spent some time on land. So they still can walk on their flippers, but their bodies are streamlined for swimming and they have valves on their noses to keep the water out. They are brown or dull black in color.

Some members of the seal family—and sea lions belong to the seal family— find it difficult to get about on land. In fact, most seals hump along on their bellies, having no other way of moving on land.

True seals have no outer ears but only holes in the sides of their heads. Sea lions, however, are known as the "eared seals," because they have small protruding ears. They also are termed "California seals," and they are the "trained seals" one sees in the circus and on the stage. They have a great sense of balance and can juggle a ball or feather on the tips of their noses and do many other tricks.

Sea lions are found mostly in the Pacific Ocean along the coast of upper California. They live on fish, and it has been estimated that a sea lion can eat almost one-tenth of his weight. A sea lion weighing five hundred pounds can eat forty pounds of fish at one "sitting."

Buster and Betty are fed fish in the zoo. They are expert in catching the fish tossed to them in their mouths.

Both Buster and Betty are very gentle and like to be petted and made much of by humans. But their greatest fun is sliding into the water and chasing each other around the pool.

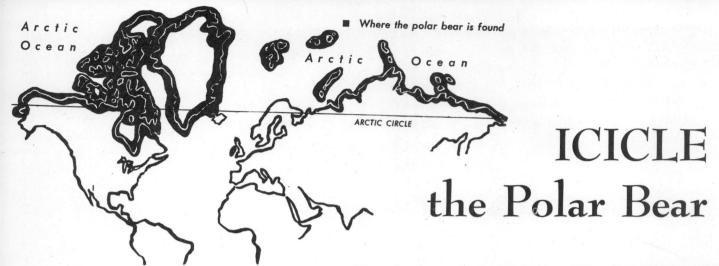

ICICLE
the Polar Bear

THERE ARE MANY PEOPLE who shake their heads sadly when Icicle, the polar bear, begins an odd series of exercises in her cage. She walks exactly six steps forward, stops, swings her head from side to side, and then backs up six steps. In going backward, her feet are placed in the same tracks she made going forward.

Icicle keeps this up for a long time, walking forward and then backward—forward and then backward. . . .

"The poor creature," some people will say. "She is unhappy in that small cage. She would like to get out in the open and run around like other animals."

This is one of the most common mistakes people make about polar bears. If they could see the bears in the arctic regions, where polar bears live, they would be surprised to see them act in exactly the same way. The bears might be on an iceberg, or on the snow-covered land. Yet they would start walking forward and backward in the same way at certain times of day.

This walking is what we call their "exercise pattern." It is the way they take their "daily dozen." If you will observe other animals, you will see that they, too, have certain little exercises peculiar to themselves.

So Icicle is only enjoying herself, and she has been happily and contentedly doing the same thing in the Lincoln Park Zoo for some twenty-eight years. She has walked forward and backward for many, many miles, and even has worn a sort of smooth path in the concrete floor of her cage.

Icicle and her mate, Snowball—who is about seven years younger—do not mind the hot weather, either, as many believe. When the summer sun beats down on their cream-white coats, the bears do not appear to notice it. This is because the white fur reflects the heat and they do not feel it nearly so much as animals with darker fur.

Then, too, in the open cage there is a water spray under which they sit in the summer. In the rear of the cage there is a small, dark den into which they can retire and keep cool if they wish.

Icicle is one of the popular attractions at the zoo. Like other bears she knows how to put on an act to get visitors to throw dainties into her cage. She stands up and waves her arms invitingly. The thing she likes best of all is chocolate-covered ice-cream bars. She is fond, too, of peanuts and Crackerjack. A few thoughtful people bring dandelion greens and endive for both Icicle and Snowball, and the bears quickly show their appreciation—by eating the offerings with relish.

Icicle and Snowball act toward each other in the cage much as they would if they were in their native icebound and snow-covered homeland. It would appear that they have an agreement not to bother each other—a sort of "armed truce." Icicle, particularly, remains in her place and does not push her lord and master too far. Otherwise she might receive a warning growl and a swift paw in the neck.

We have never had polar bear cubs in our zoo. While we have grizzly bear cubs every two years, our polar bears do not seem inclined to become parents.

In the native state the female polar bear will go off by herself and hibernate, or dig in, for several months when she is going to have cubs. She will find a hill and make a hole in the snow. This happens during December or January. The baby polar bears are helpless when born and quite small. They weigh possibly a pound, and the mother holds them close to her warm body for several weeks.

The male polar bear does not hibernate. He swims out to sea and climbs on icebergs or floating blocks of ice. He can dive into the water and hold his breath for a long time. He captures seals, walruses, and fish. In the warmer, or summer, months he eats marine grass. He hunts on both land and sea.

When it is very cold, he dives into the water to get warm. If, when he comes out, the water freezes on his fur, he digs in the snow for a time.

Polar bears are also known as white bears, water bears, and ice bears. They are among the largest bears in the world. A full-grown male may measure nine feet six inches from his head to his tail and weigh from 700 to 1,600 pounds. The neck of the polar bear is longer than that of other kinds of bears, and his head sticks straight out from his neck.

Unlike ermine and arctic foxes, which are white only in the winter season, polar bears are creamy-white the year around. Their claws are black, and their feet are hairy on the soles. They are the only bears that have hair on the bottom of their feet and they have it so they will not slip on the ice. It is a kind of insulation pad, too, and keeps their feet from getting cold.

The polar bear is a powerful animal and is more than a match for other animals of the arctic region—even the caribou with his great spreading antlers. The bear's only enemies are the killer whale, which he meets when swimming out to sea, and man.

The polar bear never becomes tame in captivity. He is always dangerous, and even keepers who feed these bears every day never dare go into their cages. When Icicle sits up and waves her arms in so friendly a fashion, it would seem that she was the gentlest of creatures. She begs for her food like a pet dog. If the smallest piece of sirup-covered popcorn falls just outside her cage, she will daintily reach out and pull it in with her claws.

But as she seems to know there are only two creatures she must fear—the killer whale and the strange animal that walks on two legs—she will never become friendly. You might say it is just her nature.

DOMINO
the Fallow Deer

IF YOU WERE ASKED to catch a small fallow deer which could leap several feet into the air from a standing position, and could run like the wind, how would you go about it?

Well, it is not easy to catch your fawn without hurting it. These small creatures are very excitable—they seem to be keyed to the highest nervous pitch at all times—and while you would certainly do everything possible not to harm the fawn you were trying to catch, the greatest care would have to be taken to see that the fawn did not hurt itself.

There was a time when there was a herd of thirty-nine beautiful fallow deer at Lincoln Park Zoo. Several of them were fawns. We wanted to catch these small, delicate creatures, to put them in separate pens, so we had to plan everything carefully. We could not use a lariat for, even if the fawns were caught with the noose, they would fight to free themselves. Nor was it advisable to run them down until they were tired and could be approached and picked up. This would be bad for their hearts.

So we used a very simple and effective method to trap our fawns. We built a "squeeze chute," as the cowboys out west call it, or a sort of funnel trap. This was simply a movable wire fence erected inside and parallel to one side of the fence in the yard. One end was open. When the fawn went in the open end, that end was closed off by a trap door. The cage in which we wanted to ship the fawn opened onto this closed part, and once in there the animal was secure. When the trap was baited, the fawn would be lured into it, without being driven. We have found this method the best for catching our elusive deer.

There are three fallow deer at the zoo now. They are Domino, the stag, and Spot and Dot, the does. Domino is a proud little deer with fine, palmated antlers—antlers which, by the way, resemble those of the moose. Like most deer, neither Domino nor Spot nor Dot is gentle. They are flighty and scary, because they are born that way. In their wild state they must always be on the alert and ready to flee to safety at the slightest indication of danger.

S. Fleishman

Domino and his mates came from a private preserve in New York State. But fallow deer, though they originated on the eastern coast of the Mediterranean near Palestine, are generally thought of as European deer. They have been kept in private parks in Europe for a long time and have been taken to other countries and liberated. They are to be found even in New Zealand.

The fallow deer, so called because of its fallow color of pale yellow, is spotted with white during the summer months. However, by selective breeding there are now three kinds—the spotted, the black, and the white. Domino, Spot, and Dot are of the spotted type.

There are some sixty species of deer throughout the world. They range from the large moose down to the small musk deer. The fallow deer is medium-sized, standing about three feet high at the shoulders. There are no deer of any kind in Australia, and the small red deer is the only species found in Africa.

The white-tailed deer is found in the United States. It was long a source of food, buckskin, and other necessities for the Indian and the white pioneer. From its skin were fashioned moccasins, jackets, and breeches. It was killed in such quantities that it almost disappeared, but today it has been restored in the eastern part of the country and, to some extent, in the western parts of its range. In summer the upper parts of this deer are reddish brown and in the winter, grayish.

The mule deer also is found from the Plains region westward. It has very large ears—hence its name. The black-tailed deer of the northwest Pacific slope is now considered to be a race of the mule deer.

The common feature of most deer is their solid bone antlers. These are not horn, as horn is hollow with a core of spongy bone. When a horn is broken off, it does not grow again. But when the deer sheds his bone antlers late in the winter, new antlers begin to sprout at once. Like the moose's antlers, they are first covered with a soft, hairy skin known as "velvet." This covering is filled with blood vessels which dry out as the antlers mature, and gradually the "velvet" is rubbed off. The stem of a deer's antler is known as the "beam," and the branches are the "tines."

The antlers, besides being showy, are weapons of defense, but are mainly employed during the breeding season in battles between bucks, or male deer.

Deer belong to the ruminant, or cud-chewing, family. When chewing their cuds, they appear so thoughtful and contented that people speak of men "ruminating," when they are carefully thinking out a problem or proposition.

But there is a good reason why a deer ruminates: The deer's stomach is divided into four chambers. Nature has so arranged it that the deer can stow away all his food in a short time and then eat it at his leisure. He often has to feed in an open space where he finds little protection. So he stores away as much food as he wants and then seeks out the security of the forest. Here he can eat and chew in peace and comfort.

Observing Domino and his mates at the zoo will make one realize that the teachings of Nature are hard to forget. While the three have nothing to fear, and there are no natural enemies to bother them, they still stow away their hay, carrots, grain, and whole-wheat bread as if they had to eat on the run. Then they spend their leisure moments ruminating—or chewing their cud.

■ Where the buffalo is found

NORTH AMERICA

MOKO the Buffalo

There was snow on the ground one cold, dismal day in December. In the buffalo enclosure at the Lincoln Park Zoo ice had formed over the wallow—where, on warmer days, the buffaloes liked to roll about in the mud.

Dan Bostrom, the keeper, heard some workmen shouting and came out of the barn to see them pointing to a male and female buffalo. Both animals were trying to push something off the ice of the buffalo wallow. It appeared to be a small bunch of fur.

"Why, that's a newborn calf!" exclaimed Dan.

Sure enough, it was a baby buffalo, just born. Both father and mother were trying to get the little fellow onto his feet. Dan knew it was too weak to stand and that he had to rescue it from its excited parents—and quickly. But not one, not even Dan, dared go into the enclosure at such a time.

Among the workmen, who were putting up new fences and making repairs around the zoo, was an Oklahoman—a former cowboy.

"Get me a rope," he said. "I'll have that calf out of there in no time."

The rope was produced. The cowboy made it into a lariat. Then he twirled the loop over his head and let it fly. It settled over the small animal, and the cowboy carefully pulled on it. Slowly he brought the calf over the snow and ice to the fence, where Dan and the others were able to lift it out.

Carrying the baby buffalo in his arms, Dan took it into the warm barn. But the little fellow did not appear to have much life left in him.

"If only I had something to stimulate him and warm him up!" said Dan.

One of the workers stepped up.

"I've got some cough medicine here," he said. "I don't know what it is, but it certainly warms me up. I call it 'moko.'"

Dan knew he had to act quickly. He would have to take a chance. He got a spoon and began giving small doses of "moko" to the baby buffalo. Soon the calf began to stir and appeared to be out of danger. Dan then gave him some warm milk and wrapped him up.

"That was a close one," sighed Dan in relief. "Your 'moko' saved his life. I'm going to call him 'Moko.'"

And so Moko it was. Despite the fact that little Moko was born out of season—buffaloes usually are born in warmer weather—and despite the narrow escape he had when his parents became excited and were pushing him around on the ice and snow, Moko grew to be one of the biggest and most nearly perfect buffaloes in the country.

In fact, zoo men from all over the world have come to the Lincoln Park Zoo especially to see and admire Moko. They all say he is the largest and finest buffalo they have ever seen.

Moko now is twelve years old. He is the head of a small family. He has three female buffaloes in his herd and is the sire of a fine calf, Marshall, who promises to grow into another Moko. Marshall is named for Marshall Head, NBC cameraman for the Lincoln Park "Zooparade," shown on television every Sunday.

Buffalo—or more properly, American bison, for sometime 'way back the early settlers misnamed the animal—are not difficult to raise. They become fairly tame in captivity, too, but do have their wilder moments. Sometimes they stage a small stampede. A sudden change of weather from hot to cold, or from cold to hot, excites them and they seek to work off energy.

At such times the buffalo start galloping madly about in their enclosure. When the keeper sees this, he opens a series of gates leading into other enclosures, and the buffalo then have room to run in a large circle. After they have circled about several times, they quiet down. It is much like the way cowboys stopped a stampede of cattle in the old days. The cowboys would turn the leaders so the cattle would start "milling," or going around in a circle, and this would calm them down.

The buffalo, or bison, once roamed the western plains of the United States by the millions. They congregated in large herds and, when migrating, they moved in solid columns of tens of thousands, traveling along well-beaten buffalo trails. These trails later were used by the pioneers and eventually became roads and highways. Railroads followed some of them, too, as they were found to be the easiest way through difficult territory.

The first buffalo seen by a European is believed to have been one the great Aztec ruler, Montezuma, had in an animal collection in Mexico City. Hernando Cortes, a Spanish explorer and conquistador, saw it there in 1521 and wrote about it.

At that time, the buffalo roamed from the Appalachian Mountains to the Rockies. Later they were to be found only west of the Mississippi River, and by

1890 the herds had dwindled down to an estimated 259 animals. This disappearance of the buffalo was caused by the great slaughter of white hunters, who killed the animals for the hides only. Thousands of hunters would be at work each day, each one killing from one hundred and fifty to two hundred buffalo during a morning. Corps of skinners were kept busy.

The Plains Indians missed the buffalo more than did the white man. They believed this animal had been given to them by their Creator. They hunted the buffalo and made use of practically every part of the animal—skin, bone, flesh, and sinew—for food, clothing, and shelter. The last great uprisings of the Plains Indians came because they felt the white man was exterminating their buffalo.

Though we may console ourselves that there would be no place for the great buffalo herds on the western plains today, we must lament their shameful wanton destruction. But they have not entirely disappeared. The Department of the Interior records some 2,800 animals now in the United States on protected ranges. There are many others in zoos and private collections.

The buffalo would increase to vast numbers again today if not controlled by the government. Now the herds are kept within the limits established by range conditions.

The buffalo averages about eleven feet long and is five feet eight inches high at the shoulder. The head, neck, and forelegs are covered with long, shaggy hair, forming a sort of mane as well as a beard on the chin. The large head is supported by strong muscles. These muscles together with a lump of fat make a hump on the shoulders. The horns are short, sharp, and curved upward. They are used both for defense and for attack.

Buffalo have a keen sense of smell and in their native state were easily frightened. When they stampeded, hardly anything could stop them.

Moko has never known any other home except that at the Lincoln Park Zoo. He is gentle and will eat out of a person's hand. He likes whole-wheat bread, alfalfa hay, and other foods that are fed to cattle.

Standing before him, feeding him bread through the fence and seeing his great, shaggy head so close, is an experience few will ever forget. His head weighs as much, maybe more, than a grown man.

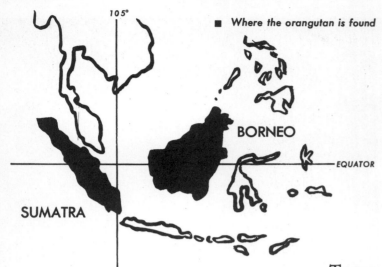

105°

BORNEO

EQUATOR

SUMATRA

LING WONG
the Orangutan

TWICE A MONTH the Monkey House is filled with happy sounds and noises. The monkeys chatter, the gibbons call shrilly, and the gorillas bark. These occasions are feast days: the days on which the monkeys and apes are given a treat.

This treat is a nice, round, juicy—and smelly—onion. The monkeys and apes snatch up their onions, tear off the skin, and eat with a relish. Some even rub their hairy coats with the onions, perhaps so that, after having finished eating, they can still have this nice smell about them. They love onions.

But not Ling Wong, the orangutan. Every time an onion is placed in Ling Wong's cage, he looks at it with suspicion. Then he gingerly rolls it around, sometimes tosses it about, and finally in disgust pushes or throws it out of his cage. He makes it very plain that he does not want an onion.

Well, there are some children who do not want their spinach. And others who do not like peas. Even if certain vegetables are placed before them which are a change of diet and are good for them, they do not want to eat them.

That is the way with Ling Wong. He is much like a child. When he was captured in the wilds of Borneo about five years ago, he, like Sinbad the gorilla, Heinie II the chimpanzee, and other small apes and monkeys, had to be treated just like an infant.

And, like an infant, he early showed that he had his own ideas about things. For no two orangutans, or other apes for that matter, are exactly the same.

I remember when I brought Ling Wong on an airplane from New York to Chicago. The Lincoln Park Zoo had obtained him from an animal dealer to whom he had been sent from Borneo. I also brought back at the same time Heine II the chimpanzee.

Before we got in the plane at New York, pictures were taken of a pretty hostess holding Ling Wong, while I held Heinie II. Then, at Chicago, another hostess posed for pictures with Ling Wong in her arms, and Heinie II and I were

in the picture, too. This was quite an experience for these airline hostesses, and both of them had a lot of trouble getting rid of Ling Wong. He held on tight—and, believe me, when you have a baby orangutan who wants to hold on to you, it is hard to get him loose. When you pry his two hands loose, he is still holding on with his feet, or when you get his feet loose, he is holding on with his hands.

Ling Wong and Heinie II became pals on that trip. They are pals to this day. They often play together but sometimes they get too rough and we have to part them. It isn't that they become angry with each other—just too enthusiastic.

The only time that Ling Wong does not like Heinie II is when Heinie II has been eating onions. But there are some people who do not like other people when *they* have been eating onions.

So, understanding Ling Wong as we do, we do not insist that he eat his onion. It is placed in his cage anyway. Someday, when he grows older, he may learn to like it and find that it is a treat just as the other apes and monkeys do.

Ling Wong is a great pet, and he likes attention. He also likes to play in his cage. He swings back and forth on a trapeze and sometimes rolls an automobile tire around as if it were a hoop. One of his favorite tricks is to stick his head through the tire and peer out at the people in front of his cage.

He is more at home on his trapeze than he is on the floor. Orangs are tree animals and seem to find it difficult to walk on the ground. They go awkwardly on all fours, walking on the sides of their feet and the knuckles of their hands.

Orangs are the redheads of the ape family. The shaggy, hairy coat of their bodies is red, or a reddish brown. You can always tell an orang by his red hair, because the hair of none of the other apes is of this color.

Like other apes, orangs have no tails. They have short, bowed hind legs and very long, strong arms, which enable them to travel through the trees in flying leaps. They can make as much speed swinging through the trees as a man can walking on the ground. Their arms are so long that, when they stand erect, they can rest the knuckles of their hands on the ground.

In Borneo, where Ling Wong was born, the Malay words *"oran utan"* mean "wild man." Besides Borneo, orangutans also are to be found in Sumatra. It is believed that there are fewer orangutans today than there are gorillas.

The grown male orang sometimes grows to be five and one-half feet tall and weighs around 250 pounds. Some of them develop a dishlike face and their cheeks spread out because of a warty growth. This makes their faces very broad and flat. They have a large pouch in the front of the throat and chest, which may extend to the armpits.

Orangs live in family groups. Baby orangs cling constantly to their mothers, holding on to their long, shaggy hair. That is why, when captured young, they cling so tightly to a human being.

The native home of these animals is the swampy forest lands at the foot of mountains. They build nests in treetops by making platforms of boughs and trees. Unlike other members of the ape family, the orangutans may occupy one home or nest several nights, instead of remaining in it for one night only.

In the wild state the orangutan's favorite food is the large jack fruit, which has a tough, spiny outer covering. But with his strong teeth he has no trouble tearing this open. He likes other fruits of the forest and eats leaves and buds, also.

At the zoo, Ling Wong is content to eat his cooked potatoes—both white and sweet potatoes—a quarter-loaf of bread (whole-wheat, please!), one-half stalk of celery, one quart of prepared milk, half an orange, or one-fourth of a grapefruit in the mornings; and five apples, a whole stalk of celery, grapes, bananas, half a head of lettuce, and a quarter-loaf of bread in the afternoons. If he seems hungry before bedtime, he gets another quarter-loaf of bread.

When it is time to retire for the night, he does not miss his home in the treetops. In the back of his cage is a little room with a shelf. When the door to this room is opened, he goes in, curls up on his shelf, and sleeps as comfortably as he would in any treetop.

AUTHOR'S NOTE

The animal stories I have told in this book introduce twenty-two zoo personalities I have known in my work. Judy, Bara, Heinie II, Fuad, and many more you have met on TV "Zooparade," and some of you have visited Icicle, Ling Wong, Moko, and others in the zoo itself. Scientists call all of the animals described in this book "mammals," because when they are babies they are fed with their mothers' milk. At the Lincoln Park Zoo we have 117 kinds of mammals, and in zoos throughout the United States there are more than 300 different types of mammals. But there are many more mammals which have never been brought to live at any zoo.

Mammals can illustrate only a part of the great animal story. Zoos also have reptile collections which include snakes, turtles, alligators, and members of the lizard family, and zoos have aviaries where birds from the world over are kept. All the inhabitants of zoos are fascinating to observe and study, and each one plays an important role in the animal story that the zoo tells.